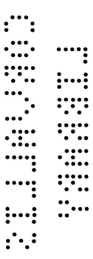

# Modern TTL Circuits Manual

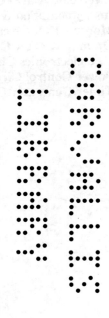

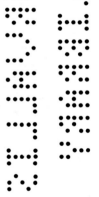

# Modern TTL Circuits Manual

## R. M. Marston

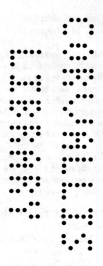

*To Esther, with love, and with gratitude for the endless patience
and unfailing kindness that she has shown me throughout the
several difficult months that it took me to evaluate and test all of
the devices and circuits described in this book and to create the
texts that accompany them.*

Newnes
An imprint of Butterworth-Heinemann Ltd
Linacre House, Jordan Hill, Oxford OX2 8DP

A member of the Reed Elsevier plc group

OXFORD   LONDON   BOSTON

MUNICH   NEW DELHI   SINGAPORE   SYDNEY

TOKYO   TORONTO   WELLINGTON

First published 1994
© R. M. Marston 1994

**British Library Cataloguing in Publication Data**
Marston, R. M.
    Modern TTL Circuits – (Circuits Manual Series)
    I. Title II. Series
    621.3815

ISBN 0 7506 2092 7

**Library of Congress Cataloguing in Publication Data**
Marston, R. M.
    Modern TTL Circuits Manual/R. M. Marston
    p. cm. – (Newnes Circuits Manual Series)
    Includes index
    ISBN 0 –7506 –2092 –7
    1. Transistor-transistor logic circuits. I. Title. II. Series.
    TK7868.L6M36 – 94-18047 CIP
    621.381'5 – dc20
Printed in Great Britain by Hartnolls Ltd, Bodmin, Cornwall

# Contents

# Preface

Modern high-speed digital electronics is dominated by two basic logic technologies, those of TTL (Transistor–Transistor Logic) and CMOS (Complementary MOSFET logic), both of which are now used in the world's leading high-speed general-purpose digital IC range, the '74' series. This unique 'Circuits Manual' book takes an in-depth look at the '74' series of ICs, concentrating mainly on its range of TTL devices but mentioning modern CMOS types where they offer special advantages. It presents the reader with over 360 outstandingly useful and carefully selected circuits, diagrams, graphs and tables, backed up by over 48 000 words of highly informative 'how it works' and 'how to use it' text and captions.

The manual is split into seven chapters. The first starts off by explaining digital IC basics, goes on to describe TTL principles, then introduces the various modern sub-families within the '74'-series range of ICs, and concludes by explaining TTL basic-usage rules, etc. Chapter 2 deals with modern logic circuitry; it starts off by looking at the symbology and mathematics of digital logic, then presents a mass of practical logic circuitry and data. The next four chapters progress through waveform generator circuitry, clocked flip-flop and counter circuits, special counter/dividers, data latches, registers, comparators and code converters. The final chapter deals with specialized types of IC such as multiplexers, demultiplexers, addressable latches, decoders, full-adders, bus transceivers, priority encoders, rate multipliers, etc.

The book, though aimed specifically at all practical design engineers, technicians and experimenters, will doubtless also be of great interest to all amateurs and students of electronics. It deals with its subject in an easy-to-read, down-to-earth, mainly non-mathematical but very comprehensive and professional manner. Each chapter starts off by explaining the basic principles of its subject and then goes on to present the reader with a great mass of practical circuits and useful data, all of which have been fully evaluated and/or verified by the author.

Throughout the volume, great emphasis is placed on practical 'user' information and circuitry, and this book, like all other volumes in the *Circuits Manual* series, abounds with useful facts and data. Most of the ICs described in the book are modestly priced and readily available types.

The reader may note that I generated all of this manual's artwork (diagrams, graphs and tables, etc.) via a standard 33mHz 486DX PC and Laserjet IIIp printer, using the excellent low-cost 'Top Draw' Windows artwork/CAD package and my own 'Top Draw' – generated sets of circuit symbols. Readers interested in the basic package may obtain further details directly from its American producers (Top Software, PO Box 1141, Conifer, CO80433, USA) or from its UK distributors (Nildram Software, 82 Akeman Street, Tring, Hertfordshire, HP23 6AF (Tel: 0442 891331).

*R. M. Marston*
*1994*

# 1 TTL principles and families

TTL (Transistor–Transistor Logic) devices are major members of the popular and internationally recognized '74' series of digital ICs (Integrated Circuits). This opening chapter starts off by explaining digital IC basics, goes on to describe TTL principles, outlines the major features of the '74' series of ICs, then introduces the various modern sub-groups of the '74' TTL family, and concludes by explaining basic TTL usage rules.

## Digital IC basics

An IC can be simply described as a complete electronic circuit or 'electronic building block' that is integrated within one or more semiconductor slices or 'chips' and encapsulated in a small multi-pin package, and which can be made fully functional by merely wiring it to a suitable power supply and connecting various pins to appropriate external input, output and auxiliary networks.

ICs, like ordinary electronic circuits, come in two basic types: they give either a 'linear' or a 'digital' type of circuit action. Linear circuits give a basic output that is directly proportional to the magnitude (analogue value) of the input signal, which itself may have any value between zero and some prescribed maximum limit. One of the simplest types of linear circuit is the unity-gain buffer; if a large sinewave signal is connected to the input of this circuit, it produces a low-impedance output of almost identical form and amplitude, as shown in *Figure 1.1a*. Linear circuits and ICs are widely used as signal processors, pre-amplifiers, power amplifiers, oscillators, etc.

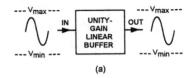

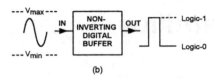

Figure 1.1  *When a large input sinewave is fed to the input of a linear buffer (a), it produces a good sinewave output, but when fed to the input of a digital buffer (b) it produces a purely digital output.*

Digital circuits, on the other hand, are effectively blind to the precise amplitudes of their input signals, and simply recognize them as being in either a 'low' or a 'high' state (usually known as 'logic-0' and 'logic-1' states respectively); their outputs similarly have only two basic states, either 'low' or 'high' (logic-0 or logic-1). One simple type of digital circuit is the non-inverting buffer; if a large sinewave signal is connected to the input of this circuit, it produces an output that (ideally) is of purely digital form, as shown in *Figure 1.1b.*

Digital circuits come in a variety of basic types, and can be built using a variety of types of discrete or integrated technologies. *Figures 1.2 to 1.7* show a selection of very simple digital buffers and 'gates' that are designed around discrete components, and which can be used in a variety of practical low- to medium-speed applications.

*Figure 1.2a* shows a simple inverting digital buffer (also known as a NOT gate), consisting of an unbiased transistor wired in the com-

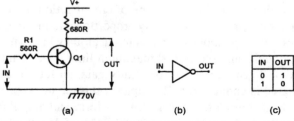

Figure 1.2  *Circuit (a), symbol (b), and Truth Table (c) of a simple inverting digital buffer.*

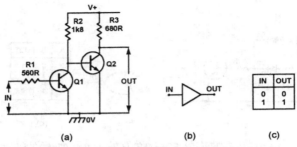

(a)  (b)  (c)

Figure 1.3  *Circuit (a), symbol (b), and Truth Table (c) of a non-inverting digital buffer.*

mon-emitter mode, and *Figure 1.2b* shows the international symbol that is used to represent it (the arrow-head indicates the direction of signal flow, and the small circle on the symbol's output indicates the 'inverting' action). The circuit action is such that Q1 is cut off (with its output high) when its input is in the zero state, and is driven fully on (with its output pulled low) when its input is high; this information is presented in concise form by the *'Truth Table'* of *Figure 1.2c*, which shows that the output is at logic-1 when the input is at logic-0, and vice versa.

*Figure 1.3a* shows a simple non-inverting digital buffer, consisting of a direct coupled pair of common-emitter (inverter) transistor stages, and *Figure 1.3b* shows the arrow-like international symbol that is used to represent it; *Figure 1.3c* shows the Truth Table that describes its action: the output is at logic-0 when the input is at logic-0, and is at logic-1 when the input is at logic-1.

In digital electronics, a 'gate' is a circuit that opens or gives an 'output' (usually defined as a 'high' or logic-1 state) only under a certain set of input conditions. *Figure 1.4a* shows a simple 2-input OR gate, made from two diodes and a resistor, and *Figure 1.4b* shown the international symbol that is used to represent it; *Figure*

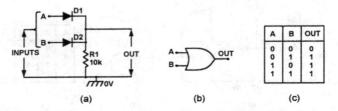

(a)  (b)  (c)

Figure 1.4  *Circuit (a), symbol (b), and Truth Table of a simple 2-input OR gate.*

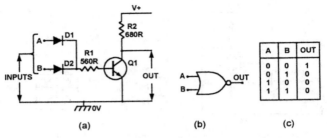

Figure 1.5  *Circuit (a), symbol (b), and Truth Table of a 2-input NOR gate.*

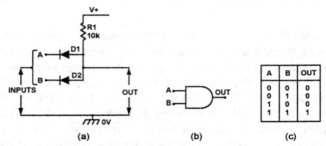

Figure 1.6  *Circuit (a), symbol (b), and Truth Table of a simple 2-input AND gate.*

*1.4c* shows its Truth Table (in which the inputs are referred to as A or B), which shows that the output goes to logic-1 if A *or* B goes to logic-1.

*Figure 1.5* shows the circuit, symbol, and Truth Table of a 2-input NOR (Negated-output OR) gate, in which the output is inverted (as indicated by the output circle) and goes to logic-0 if either input goes high.

*Figure 1.6a* shows a simple 2-input AND gate, made from two

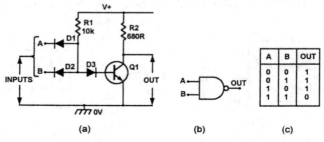

Figure 1.7  *Circuit (a), symbol (b), and Truth Table of a 2-input NAND gate.*

diodes and a resistor, and *Figure 1.6b* shows its standard international symbol; *Figure 1.6c* shows the gate's Truth Table, which indicates that the output goes to logic-1 only if inputs A *and* B are at logic-1.

Finally, *Figure 1.7* shows the circuit, symbol, and Truth Table of a 2-input NAND (Negated-output AND) gate, in which the output is inverted (as indicated by the output circle) and goes to logic-0 only if both inputs are at logic-1.

Note that although the four basic types of gate circuit described above are each shown with only two input terminals, they can in fact be designed or used to accept any desired number of inputs, and can be used to perform a variety of simple 'logic' operations. Also note that many types of digital buffer and gate are readily available in IC form, as also are many other digital circuits, including flip-flops, latches, shift registers, counters, data selectors, encoders, decoders, memories, etc. By convention, most digital ICs are also known as 'logic' ICs.

In practice, logic ICs may range from relatively simple devices housing the equivalent of just a few basic gates or buffers, to incredibly complex devices housing the equivalent of tens of thousands of interconnected gates, etc. By convention, the following general terms are used to describe the relative density or complexity of integration:

● *SSI (Small Scale Integration):* complexity level between 1 and 10 gates.
● *MSI (Medium Scale Integration):* complexity level between 10 and 100 gates.
● *LSI (Large Scale Integration):* complexity level between 100 and 1000 gates.
● *VLSI (Very Large Scale Integration):* complexity level between 1000 and 10 000 gates.
● *SLSI (Super Large Scale Integration):* complexity level between 10 000 and 100 000 gates.

## Digital waveform basics

Digital ICs are invariably used to process digital waveforms. It is thus pertinent at this point to remind the reader of some basic facts and terms concerning digital waveforms, which are available in

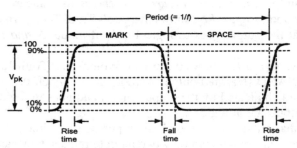

Figure 1.8  *Basic parameters of a squarewave.*

either square or pulse form. *Figure 1.8* illustrates the basic parameters of a squarewave; in each cycle the wave first switches from zero to some peak voltage value ($V_{pk}$) for a fixed period, and then switches low again for a second fixed period, and so on. The time taken for the waveform to rise from 10% to 90% of $V_{pk}$ is known as its *rise time*, and that taken for it to drop from 90% to 10% of $V_{pk}$ is known as its *fall time*. In each squarewave cycle, the 'high' part is known as its *mark* and the 'low' part as its *space*. In a symmetrical squarewave such as that shown, the mark and space periods are equal and the waveform is said to have a 1:1 Mark–Space (or M–S) ratio, or a 50 per-cent duty cycle (since the mark duration forms 50% of the total cycle period). Squarewaves are not necessarily symmetrical, but are always free-running or repetitive, i.e., they cycle repeatedly, with sharply defined mark and space periods.

A pulse waveform can be roughly described as being a bit like a squarewave (complete with rise and fall times, etc.) but with only its mark or its space period sharply defined, the duration of the remaining period being unimportant. *Figure 1.9a* shows a basic 'positive-going' pulse waveform, which has a 'rising' or positive-going leading edge, and *Figure 1.9b* shows a 'negative-going' pulse waveform, which has a 'falling' or negative-going leading edge. Note that many

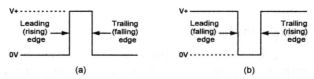

Figure 1.9  *Basic forms of (a) 'positive-going' and (b) 'negative-going' pulses.*

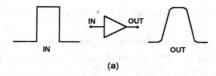

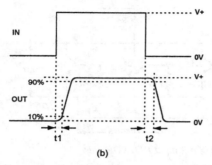

**(b)**

Figure 1.10  *A perfect pulse, fed to the input of a practical amplifier or gate, produces an output pulse that is distorted both in form and time; the output pulse's time delay is called its 'propagation delay', and (in 'b') = $(t_1+t_2)/2$.*

modern MSI digital ICs such as counter/dividers and shift registers, for example, can be selected or programmed to trigger on either the rising or the falling edge of an input pulse, as desired by the user.

If a near-perfect pulse waveform is fed to the input of a real-life amplifier or gate, etc., the resulting output waveform will be distorted both in form and time, as shown in *Figure 1.10*. Thus, not only will the output waveform's rise and fall times be increased, but the arrival and termination of the output pulse will be time-delayed relative to that of the input pulse; the mean value of the delays is called the device's *propagation delay*. Also, the peaks of the waveform's rising and falling edges may suffer from various forms of 'ringing' or 'overshoot' or 'undershoot', etc.; the magnitudes of all of these

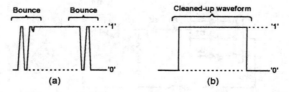

Figure 1.11  *Mechanically-derived pulse waveforms often suffer from 'contact bounce' (a), and must be cleaned-up (b) before use.*

distortions varies with the quality or structure of the amplifier or gate, etc.

In practice, pulse input waveforms may sometimes be so imperfect that they may need to be 'conditioned' before they are suitable for use by modern fast-acting digital ICs. Specifically, they may have

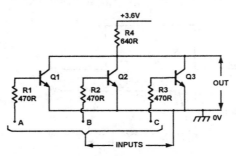

Figure 1.12   *IC version of a 3-input RTL NOR gate.*

such long rise or fall times that they may have to be sharpened up via a Schmitt trigger before they are suitable for use. Again, many mechanically-derived 'pulse' waveforms such as those generated via switches or contact-breakers, etc., may suffer from severe multiple 'contact bounce' problems such as those shown in *Figure 1.11a*, in which case they will have to be converted to the 'clean' form shown in *Figure 1.11b* before they can be usefully used, etc.

## Basic logic-IC families

Practical digital logic circuits and ICs can be built by using various technologies. The first successful family of digital ICs appeared in the mid-1960s; these used a 3.6V supply and employed a simple

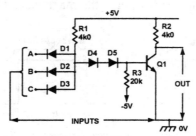

Figure 1.13   *IC version of a 3-input DTL NAND gate.*

technology that became known as Resistor-Transistor Logic, or RTL. *Figure 1.12* shows the basic circuit of a 3-input RTL NOR gate. RTL was rather slow in operation, having a typical propagation delay (the time taken for a single pulse edge or transition to travel from input to output) of 40ns in a low-power gate, or 12ns in a medium-power gate. RTL is now obsolete.

Another early type of IC logic technology, developed in the late 1960s, was based on simple developments of the discrete types of logic circuit shows in *Figures 1.2* to *1.7*, and was known as Diode–Transistor Logic, or DTL. *Figure 1.13* shows the basic circuit of a 3-input DTL NAND gate. DTL used a dual 5-volt power supply, gave a typical propagation delay of 30ns, and gave an output of less than 0.4V in the '0' state and greater than 3.5V in the '1' state. DTL is now obsolete.

Between the late 1960s and mid-1970s, several other promising IC logic technologies appeared, most of them soon disappearing back into oblivion. Amongst those that came and either went or receded in importance were HTL (High Threshold Logic), ECL (Emitter Coupled Logic), and PML (P-type MOSFET Logic). At that time, the basic aim of digital IC designers was to devise a technology that was simple to use and which gave a good compromise between high operating speed and low power consumption. The problem here was that conventional transistor-type circuitry, using an output stage of the *Figure 1.2* type (as in RTL and DTL systems, for example) was simply not capable of meeting the last two of these design needs. Specifically, remembering that all practical output loads inevitably contain capacitance (typically up to about 30pF in most digital circuits), it can be seen that the *Figure 1.2* circuit will charge (source current into) a capacitive load fairly slowly via R2 when Q1 is turned off, but will discharge it (sink current from it) rapidly via Q1's collector when Q1 is turned on; thus, circuits of this type produce digital outputs that tend to have long rise times and short fall times; the only way to reduce the rise time is to reduce the R2 value, and that increases Q1's current consumption by a proportionate amount.

Note that one good way of describing the deficiency of the *Figure 2.1* logic circuit is to say that its output gives an active pull-down action (via Q1), but a passive pull-up action (via R2). Obviously, an ideal digital output stage would be one that gives both active pull-up and active pull-down action, with the ability to both source and sink high currents and thus give the required fast heavy-load output-switching action, but with only one of these actions enabled at any

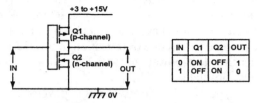

Figure 1.14   *Circuit and Truth Table of a basic CMOS inverter.*

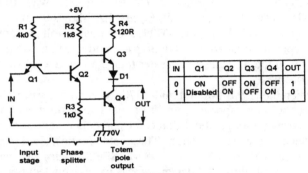

Figure 1.15   *Circuit and Truth Table of a basic TTL inverter.*

given moment, thus giving a reasonably low mean current consumption. In the 1970s, two such technologies hit the commercial market like a bombshell, and went on to form the basis of today's two dominant digital IC families. The first of these, based on bipolar transistor technology, is known as TTL (Transistor–Transistor Logic), and formed the basis of the so-called '74' family of digital IC that first arrived in 1972. The second, based on FET technology, is known as CMOS (Complementary *MOS*FET logic), and forms the basis of the rival '4000-series' (and the similar '4500-series') digital IC family that first arrived in about 1975. The TTL and CMOS technologies have vastly different characteristics, but both offer specific technical advantages that make them invaluable in particular applications.

The most significant differences between the technologies of CMOS and TTL ICs can be seen in their basic inverter/buffer networks, which are used (sometimes in slightly modified form) in virtually every IC within the family range of each type of device. *Figures 1.14* and *1.15* show the two different basic designs.

The CMOS inverter of *Figure 1.14* consists of a complementary pair of MOSFETs, wired in series, with p-channel MOSFET Q1 at the top and n-channel MOSFET Q2 below, and with both high-impedance gates joined together. The pair can be powered from any supply in the 3V to 15V range. When the circuit's input is at logic-0, the basic action is such that Q1 is driven on and Q2 is cut off, and the output is actively pulled high (to logic-1); note that the output can source (drive) fairly high currents into an external load (via Q1) under this condition, but that the actual inverter stage consumes near-zero current, since Q2 is cut off. When the circuit's input is at logic-1, the reverse of this action occurs, and Q1 is cut off and Q2 is driven on, and the output is actively pulled low (to logic-0); note that the output can sink (absorb) fairly high currents from an external load (via Q2) under this condition, but that the actual inverter stage consumes near-zero current, since Q1 is cut off.

Thus, the basic CMOS inverter can be used with any supply in the 3V to 15V range, has a very high input impedance, consumes near-zero quiescent current, has an output that switches almost fully between the two supply rails, and can source or sink fairly high output load currents. Typically, a single basic CMOS stage has a propagation delay of about 12 to 60 nS, depending on supply voltage.

The TTL inverter of *Figure 1.15* is split into three sections, consisting of an emitter-driven input (Q1), a phase-splitter (Q2), and a 'totem-pole' output stage (Q3–D1–Q4), and must be powered from a 5V supply. When the circuit's input is pulled down to logic-0, the basic action is such that Q1 is saturated, thus depriving Q2 of base current and causing Q2 and Q4 to cut off, and at the same time causing emitter-follower Q3 to turn on via R2 and give an active pull-up action in which the output has (because of various volt-drops) a typical loaded value of about 3.5V and can source fairly high currents into an external load. Conversely, when the circuit's input is at logic-1, Q1 is disabled, allowing Q2 to be driven on via R1 and the forward-biased base-collector junction of Q1, thus driving Q4 to saturation and simultaneously cutting-off Q3; under this condition Q4 gives an active pull-down action and can sink fairly high currents, and the output takes up a typical loaded value of 400mV. Note that (ignoring external load currents) the circuit consumes a quiescent current of about 1mA in the logic-1 output state, and 3mA in the logic-0 output state.

Thus, the basic TTL inverter can only be used with a 5V supply, has a very low input impedance, consumes up to 3mA of quiescent current, has an output that does not switch fully between the two supply rails, and can source or sink fairly high load currents. Typically, a single basic TTL stage has a propagation delay of about 12nS.

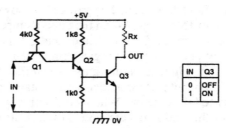

Figure 1.16   *TTL inverter with open collector output.*

## Basic TTL circuit variations

There are five very important variations of the basic *Figure 1.15* TTL 'inverter' circuit. The simplest of these is the so-called 'open collector' TTL circuit, which is shown in basic form in *Figure 1.16*. Here, output transistor Q3 is cut off when the input is at logic-0, and is driven on when the input is at logic-1. Thus, by wiring an external load resistor between the 'OUT' and '+5V' pins, the circuit can be used as a 'passive pull-up' voltage inverter that has an output that (when lightly loaded) switches almost fully between zero and the positive supply rail value. Alternatively, it can be used to drive an external load (such as a LED or relay) that is connected between 'OUT' and a positive supply rail, in which case the load activates when a logic-1 input is applied.

The second variation is the non-inverting amplifier or buffer. This is made by simply wiring an additional direct-coupled inverter stage between the phase-splitter and output stages of the standard inverter. *Figure 1.17* shows an 'open collector' version of such a circuit, which can be used with an external resistor or load; in this example, Q4 turns on when a logic-0 input is applied.

*Figure 1.18* shows a major TTL design variation. Here, the basic

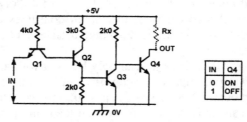

Figure 1.17   *TTL non-inverting buffer with open-collector output.*

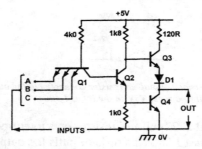

Figure 1.18 *TTL 3-input NAND gate.*

inverter circuit is used with a triple-emitter input transistor, to make a 3-input NAND gate in which the output goes low (to logic-0) only when all three inputs are high (in the logic-1 state). In practice, multiple-emitter transistors are widely used within TTL ICs; some TTL gates use an input transistor with as many as a dozen emitters, to make a 12-input gate.

A further variation concerns the use of a 'Tri-State' or '3-state' type of output that incorporates additional networks plus an external ENABLE control terminal, which in one state allows the totem-pole output stage to operate in its normal 'logic-0 or logic-1' mode, but in the other state disables (turns off) both totem-pole transistors and thus gives an open-circuit (high impedance) output. This facility is useful in allowing several outputs or inputs to be shorted to a common bus or line, as shown in *Figure 1.19*, and to communicate along that line by ENABLING only one output and one input device at a time.

The final circuit variation is an 'application' one, and concerns the

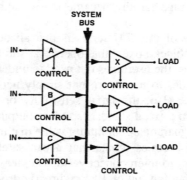

Figure 1.19 *'Tri-State' logic enables several outputs or inputs to be connected to a common bus; only one output/input must be made active at any given moment.*

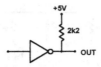

Figure 1.20  *An external 2k2 pull-up resistor connected to the output of a totem-pole stage pulls the output to almost +5V in the logic-1 state.*

use of an external 2k2 'pull-up' resistor on a totem-pole output stage, as shown in *Figure 1.20*. This resistor pulls the output (when lightly loaded) up to virtually the full +5V supply value when the output is in the logic-1 state, rather than to only +3.5V; this is sometimes useful when interfacing the output of a TTL IC to the input of a CMOS IC, etc.

## The '74' series of digital ICs

TTL IC technology first hit the electronics engineering scene in a big way in about 1972, when it suddenly arrived in the form of an entire range of versatile and cleverly conceived digital ICs that were each designed to operate from a single-ended 5V supply and to directly and easily interconnect with each other (each output was capable of directly driving several inputs), thus making it relatively easy for any moderately competent engineer to design and develop fairly complex digital logic circuits. It was an instant and brilliant international success, and almost immediately became the world's leading IC logic system. Its ICs were produced in both commercial and military grades, and carried prefixes of '74' and '54' respectively; the commercial product range rapidly became known simply as the '74'-series of ICs.

A major feature of the '74' series is that all devices within the range function as 'black boxes' that operate at similar input and output threshold levels; the user does not need to understand their internal circuitry in order to use them, but simply needs to know their basic usage rules. Also, the input sensitivity or 'fan-in' of each device conforms to a fixed standard, and its output drive capability or 'fan-out' has a guaranteed minimum value that indicates the number of external '74'-series inputs that it can safely directly drive, making it very easy to interconnect various devices; thus, the output of a '74' gate with a fan-out of 10 can directly drive as many as ten parallel-connected standard inputs on other '74'-series ICs.

The type of TTL technology used in the initial (1972) '74'-series ICs resulted in a range of devices that were moderately fast but consumed fairly heavy currents. Within a year or so, sub-families of the original TTL were introduced, offering a trade-off between speed and power, i.e. twice the speed but at twice the current consumption (in the 'H' or 'high speed' sub-family), or one-tenth of the current consumption but only one-third of the normal speed (in the 'L' or 'low power' sub-family), for example. This trend of seeking a good or ever-better trade-off between speed and power consumption has continued until the present day, and so far a total of eight commercially successful sub-families of TTL (and five sub-families of CMOS) have appeared in the '74' series of digital ICs. Many of these sub-families have subsequently become obsolete or obsolescent, but the practical design/maintenance engineer or technician still needs a basic knowledge of all of them, since he or she will often meet them in old equipment that needs repairing or up-grading.

Note that each sub-family of the '74' series of ICs is almost directly compatible with all other sub-families in the series. Thus, if you open up an old piece of equipment and find (for example) that an old '74L90' decade counter IC needs replacing but is no longer available, you will probably find that a modern '74LS90' decade counter IC can be used as a direct plug-in replacement, or that any other '74XX90' IC can be used as a replacement either directly or with slight circuit modification (depending on the basic characteristics of

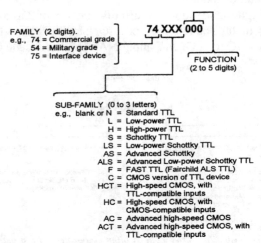

Figure 1.21 *Basic coding system used on the '74'-series ICs.*

the two sub-families). In either case, the first thing that you will need to do is identify the device of interest, from its printed code number. *Figure 1.21* explains the basic scheme that is used in formatting the '74'-series code numbers.

All ICs in the '74' family are identified by an alphanumeric code which, in its simplest form, consists of three sub-codes strung together as shown in *Figure 1.21*. The first (left hand) sub-code consists of two digits that read either 74, 54 or 75. '74' identifies the IC as a commercial-grade member of the family; these devices are usually encapsulated in a plastic 14-pin, 16-pin, or 24-pin dual-in-line package (DIP), can be used with supplies within the limit +4.75V to +5.25V, and can be operated over the temperature range 0°C to +70°C. '54' identifies the IC as a high-quality military-grade member of the family; these devices are encapsulated in exotic packages, can use supplies within the limit +4.5V to +5.5V, and can operate over the temperature range -55°C to +125°C. '75' identifies the IC as a commercial-grade interface device that is designed to support the '74' range of devices.

The second (central) sub-code consists of up to three letters, and identifies the precise technology or sub-family used in the construction of the device, as shown in the diagram. Note that standard TTL devices carries either no central code at all, or an 'N'; each of the other seven major TTL sub-family devices carries a central identifying code, and the five major CMOS '74' sub-families carry a central code that includes the letter 'C'.

The last (right-hand) sub-code usually consists of 2 to 5 digits (but occasionally includes a letter 'A' or a star), and identifies the precise function of the IC (e.g. Quad 2-input NAND gate, decade counter, 4-

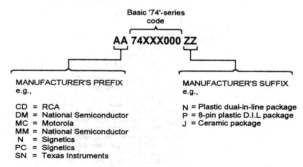

Figure 1.22 *The basic '74'-series code is often elaborated with a manufacturer's prefix and/or suffix.*

bit shift register, etc.). The precise relationship between this sub-code and the device function can be ascertained from manufacturer's lists.

Thus, a '74' type of IC may carry a code that, in its simplest form, reads something like 7400, 74N00, 7414, etc., if it is a standard TTL device, or 74L14, 74LS38, 74HC03, etc., if it is some other sub-member of the '74' family. Note that in practice '74'-series ICs often carry an elaborated form of the basic code that includes a two-letter prefix that identifies the manufacturer, plus a lettered manufacturer's suffix that indicates the packaging style, etc., as shown in *Figure 1.22*. Hence, a device marked SN74LS90N is a normal 74LS90 IC, manufactured by Texas Instruments and housed in a plastic dual-in-line package.

## TTL sub-families

Eight major sub-families of TTL have been used in the '74'-series throughout its lifetime, as follows:

*Standard TTL.* Standard TTL is similar to the basic type already described, except that each of its inputs is provided with a protection diode that helps suppress transients and speed up its switching action. *Figure 1.23* shows the actual circuit of a 7400 2-input NAND gate; its power consumption is 10mW, and its propagation delay is 9ns when driving a 15pF/400R load.

*Low-power (L) TTL (now obsolete).* Low-power TTL is a modified version of the standard type, with its resistance values greatly increased to give a dramatic reduction in power consumption at the

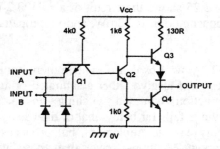

Figure 1.23   *Circuit of a Standard TTL 7400 2-input NAND gate.*

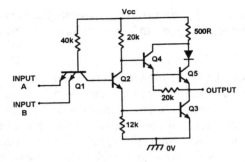

Figure 1.24   *Circuit of a low-power (L) TTL 74L00 2-input NAND gate.*

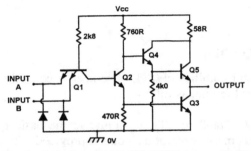

Figure 1.25   *Circuit of a high-speed (H) TTL 74H00 2-input NAND gate.*

expense of reduced speed. *Figure 1.24* shows the circuit of a 74L00 2-input NAND gate; its power consumption is 1mW, and its propagation delay is typically 33ns.

*High-speed (H) TTL (now obsolete).* High-speed TTL is a modified version of the standard type, with its resistance values reduced to give an increase in speed at the expense of increased power consumption. *Figure 1.25* shows the circuit of a 74H00 2-input NAND gate; its power consumption is 22mW, and its propagation delay is typically 6nS.

*Schottky (S) TTL (now obsolete).* A common-emitter transistor switch can be designed to give either a saturated or an unsaturated type of switching action. Saturated switching – in which the transistor's collector voltage falls far below that of the base under the 'on' condition – is very easy to implement, but produces propagation delays that are about 2.5 times longer than those available from

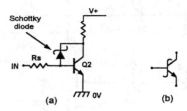

(a)                    (b)

Figure 1.26 *(a) a Schottky diode used to limit the saturation depth of an npn transistor; (b) symbol of an npn 'Schottky' transistor, with a built-in clamping diode between its collector and base.*

unsaturated circuits. Standard TTL operates its transistors in a heavily-saturated switching mode in which the collector falls some 400mV below the base under the 'on' condition, and is thus intrinsically fairly slow. Schottky TTL, on the other hand, operates its transistors in a lightly-saturated switching mode in which the collector only falls some 180mV below the base voltage under the 'on; condition, and is almost as fast as an unsaturated circuit. Basically, this action is achieved by connecting a Schottky diode (which is fast-acting and typically has a forward volt drop of only 180mV) between the transistor's collector and base as shown in *Figure 1.26a*, in which $R_S$ represents the input pulse's source impedance. Thus, if the collector goes more than 180mV negative to the base, the Schottky diode becomes forward biased and starts to shunt base current directly into the transistor's collector, thus automatically preventing deeper saturation. In reality, the Schottky diode can easily be

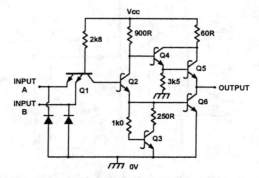

Figure 1.27 *Circuit of a Schottky (S) TTL 74S00 2-input NAND gate.*

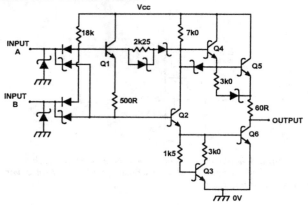

Figure 1.28  *Circuit of a low-power Schottky (LS) 74LS00 2-input NAND gate.*

incorporated in the transistor's structure, and a 'Schottky-clamped transistor' of this type uses the symbol shown in *Figure 1.26b*.

In a practical Schottky TTL IC, Schottky-clamped transistors are widely used, and most resistance values are reduced, thus giving a good increase in speed at the expense of power consumption. The totem-pole output stage uses a Darlington transistor pair to give active pull-up, plus a modified active pull-down network that gives an improved waveform-squaring action. *Figure 1.27* shows the circuit of a 74S00 2-input NAND gate; its power consumption is 20mW and its propagation delay is 3ns when driving a 15pF/280R load.

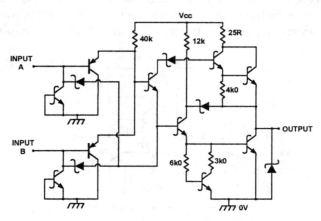

Figure 1.29  *Circuit of an advanced low-power Schottky (ALS) 74ALS00 2-input NAND gate.*

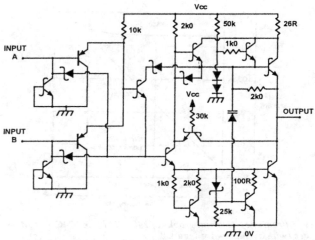

Figure 1.30   *Circuit of an advanced Schottky (AS) TTL 74AS00 2-input NAND gate.*

*Low-power Schottky (LS) TTL.* Low-power Schottky uses a modified form of Schottky technology, using improved manufacturing techniques, combined with a 'diode-transistor' (rather than multi-emitter) form of input network that has a high impedance and gives fast switching. *Figure 1.28* shows the circuit of a 74LS00 2-input NAND gate; its power consumption is 2mW and its propagation delay is 8ns when driving a 12p/2k0 load.

*Advanced low-power Schottky (ALS) TTL.* This sub-family is similar to LS but uses an advanced fabrication process which, combined with minor design modifications, yields active devices that are faster and have higher gains than LS types. *Figure 1.29* shows the circuit of a 74ALS00 2-input NAND gate; its power consumption is 1mW and its propagation delay is 4ns when driving a 50p/2k0 load.

*Advanced Schottky (AS) TTL.* This sub-family is similar to ALS, but its design is optimized to give very high speed at the expense of power consumption. *Figure 1.30* shows the circuit of a 74AS00 2-input NAND gate; its power consumption is 22mW and its propagation delay is a mere 2ns when driving a 50p/2k0 load.

*Fast (F) TTL.* FAST (Fairchild Advanced Schottky TTL) is Fairchild's version of 'AS' TTL. It is manufactured under licence by

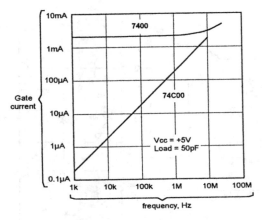

Figure 1.31   *Frequency - current graphs of 7400 (TTL) and 74C00 (CMOS) 2-input NAND gates (with a squarewave input).*

several companies (including Philips and National Semiconductors); its performance is similar (in terms of speed and power consumption) to that of the AS sub-family.

## CMOS '74'-series sub-families.

When the '74' series of IC was first released in 1972, all devices in the range were based on bipolar TTL technology, which inherently consumes a fairly large amount of power irrespective of its operating speed. In about 1975 the rival CMOS digital ICs technology arrived on the scene, and although not as fast as TTL it offered the outstanding advantage of having a power consumption that was directly proportional to operating speed, being virtually zero under quiescent conditions and rising to the same value as TTL at about 10MHz. In the late 1970s CMOS was introduced as a sub-family within the '74'-series range of devices, carrying the central code 'C'; the graph of *Figure 1.31* compares the frequency/current-consumption curves of a single gate from the standard TTL and the CMOS 'C' versions of the 7400 quad 2-input NAND gate IC.

In its early form, the '74'-series 'C' sub-family was slow and had a very weak output-drive capability (its fan-out drive was equal to two 'L' type inputs). In subsequent years, however, considerable improvements took place in both the design and production of

CMOS-type devices, and so far a total of five CMOS sub-families have been introduced in the '74' series, as follows:

*Standard (C) CMOS (now obsolete).* This sub-family was virtually normal CMOS in a '74'-series format. Typically, a single 74C00 2-input NAND gate consumed about 15mW at 10MHz, and had a propagation delay of 60ns.

*High-speed (HC) CMOS.* In the early 1980s, advances in CMOS fabrication techniques yielded speed performances similar to LS TTL, but with CMOS levels of power consumption. HC '74'-series devices using this technology have CMOS-compatible inputs; typically, a single 74HC00 2-input NAND gate consumes less than 1μA of quiescent current, and has a propagation delay of 8nS.

*High-speed (HCT) CMOS.* These are HC-type devices, but have TTL-compatible inputs. Typically, a 74HCT00 2-input NAND gate consumes less than 1μA of quiescent current and has a propagation delay of 18ns.

*Advanced High-speed (AC) CMOS.* In the late 1980s, advances in CMOS design and further advances in CMOS fabrication techniques yielded speed performance similar to those of ALS. AC '74'-series devices using this technology have CMOS-compatible inputs; typically, a 74AC00 2-input NAND gate has a propagation delay of 5ns.

*Advanced High Speed? (ACT) CMOS.* These are AC-type devices, but have TTL-compatible inputs. Typically, a 74ACT00 2-input NAND gate has a propagation delay of 7ns.

## Which sub-family is best?

From the point of view of the electronics engineer who is designing a new commercial product, logic ICs should always be selected on a basis of commercial – rather than purely technical – superiority. It would, for example, be foolish to use a really fast ALS gate in an application in which a slower LS or HC device would be perfectly adequate and was easily available at a fraction of the cost of the ALS device. Similarly, if the product is expected to have a fairly long sales life, the designer should use only ICs that are multi-sourced (available from several manufacturers) and likely to have a long produc-

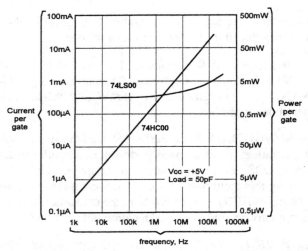

Figure 1.32  *Frequency versus current/power graphs of 74LS00 and 74HC00 2-input NAND gates (with a squarewave input).*

tion life, and should not use devices that are single-sourced or are unproven in terms of viability or reliability.

With the above points in mind, note that the five '74'-series IC sub-families most widely available at the time of writing are Standard and LS TTL, and HC, HCT and AC CMOS. Of these, Standard TTL is technically and commercially inferior to LS and is not recommended for use in new designs, AC CMOS costs approximately 2.5 times as much as LS TTL or HC/HCT CMOS and should thus only be used in special applications, and HCT is only meant to be used as a replacement for TTL devices in existing designs and should not (since it is not good practice to mix TTL and CMOS devices unnecessarily) be used in new designs. That leaves just LS TTL and HC CMOS.

Of these two '74'-series sub-families, LS is slightly faster than HC and is available in a far greater range of functional device types, but generally consumes more supply current/power than HC at frequencies below about 5MHz (*Figure 1.32* compares the performances of 74LS00 and 74HC00 gates). Thus, for most 'new design' applications, the LS TTL and HC CMOS sub-families deserve a joint 'best' award, with a slight edge perhaps going to LS. Note that, since this book is concerned mainly with modern TTL devices, little further mention will be made of CMOS ICs; most of the practical circuits in this volume are based on LS TTL ICs.

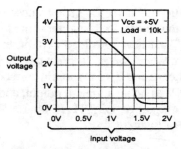

Figure 1.33  *Standard-TTL input-to-output voltage graph.*

## TTL logic levels and noise immunity

All digital ICs handle input and output signals that are in either the 'high' (logic-1) or 'low' (logic-0) states. In practice, each of these 'logic levels' must fall within a defined range of voltage limits. *Figure 1.33*, for example, shows the typical input-to-output voltage curve of a simple Standard TTL inverter that operates from a +5V supply and has a lightly loaded output. Note that the output is 'high', at +3.5 volts, until the input voltage rises to 0.7V, and then falls fairly linearly as the input is further increased, and eventually stabilizes at a 'low' value of about 0.25V when the input rises above 1.5V. In practice, all Standard and LS TTL ICs are, when using a +5V supply, guaranteed to recognize any input voltage of up to 0.8V as being a logic-0 input, and of 2.0V or above as being a logic-1 input; note that the area between these two levels is known as the IC's 'indeterminate' zone or region, and operation within this zone should be avoided at any cost.

In TTL circuitry, different logic levels are used to define input and output signals, since TTL output voltage levels vary considerably

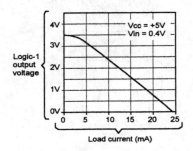

Figure 1.34  *Standard-TTL 'logic-1' output voltage - current graph.*

with loading conditions; *Figure 1.34* shows how – when an input of 0.4V is applied to the above TTL inverter – the logic-1 output voltage falls from +3.5V at near-zero load current, to a mere 2.0V at a load current of 13mA, and so on. In practice, all Standard TTL ICs are guaranteed (when using a +5V supply) to recognize any output voltage of up to 0.4V as being a logic-0 output, and of 2.4V or above as being a logic-1 output; on LS TTL ICs these levels are 0.5V for logic-0, and 2.7V for logic-1.

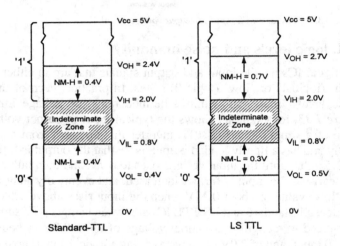

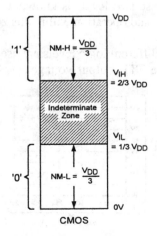

Figure 1.35   *Logic level and noise margin values of Standard TTL, LS TTL, and CMOS.*

| PARAMETER | '74'-Series TTL Sub-families | | | | | | | UNITS |
|---|---|---|---|---|---|---|---|---|
|  | Standard | L | H | S | LS | AS | ALS |  |
| Propagation Delay (2-input NAND gate) | 9nS | 33 | 6 | 3 | 8 | 2 | 4 | nS |
| Power Dissipation (per gate) | 10mW | 1 | 22 | 20 | 2 | 22 | 1 | mW |
| $V_{IH}$ | 2.0V | 2.0 | 2.0 | 2.0 | 2.0 | 2.0 | 2.0 | V |
| $V_{OH}$ | 2.4V | 2.4 | 2.4 | 2.7 | 2.7 | Vcc-2V | Vcc-2V | V |
| NM-H | 400mV | 400 | 400 | 700 | 700 | 700 | 700 | mV |
| $V_{IL}$ | 0.8V | 0.7 | 0.8 | 0.8 | 0.8 | 0.8 | 0.8 | V |
| $V_{OL}$ | 0.4V | 0.3 | 0.4 | 0.5 | 0.5 | 0.5 | 0.5 | V |
| NM-L | 400mV | 300 | 400 | 300 | 300 | 300 | 300 | mV |

Figure 1.36   *Typical propagation delay and power dissipation figures for single '00'-type NAND gates within the TTL sub-family ranges, together with sub-family voltage threshold and noise-margin values.*

When one TTL output is connected directly to a following TTL input, any excessive 'noise' on the output signal may cause incorrect operation of the following input stage. Thus, taking a worst-case situation, a logic-1 Standard TTL output may be as low as 2.4V, and any superimposed negative-going 'noise' pulse greater than 0.4V will drive the following input below the 2.0V 'logic-0' defined threshold and may cause it to erroneously recognize its input as being a logic-0 (rather than logic-1) signal. The maximum worst-case magnitude of noise that a digital IC can ignore under these conditions is known as its 'noise immunity' or 'noise margin' value, and equals the difference between the logic-0 or logic-1 output/input threshold values. With Standard TTL, noise margins for both logic-1 (NM-H) and logic-0 (NM-L) have defined worst-case values of 400mV; with LS TTL, the noise margins are 700mV for logic-1, and 300mV for logic-0; with CMOS, both margins have values of $V_{DD}/3$. *Figure 1.35* illustrates the values of these three sets of threshold and margin values.

*Figure 1.36* expands the above information and shows actual defined threshold voltage and noise margin values, together with typical progagation and power disspitation values for single '00'-type 2-input NAND gates, for the seven major sub-families of TTL (FAST TTL is regarded here as simply a minor variation of AS TTL).

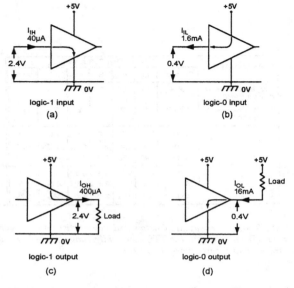

Figure 1.37  *Basic input and output parameters of a Standard TTL logic element.*

## Fan-in and fan-out

In TTL circuitry, an element's input drive requirements are known as its 'fan-in' values, and its output driving capability limits are known as its 'fan-out' values. *Figure 1.37* illustrates the meanings and worst-case values of these items when applied to a Standard TTL element. Thus, *Figure 1.37a* shows that when the TTL element is driven from a Standard TTL output stage, it draws a worst-case input current ($I_{IH}$) of 40µA when fed with a 2.4V logic-1 input, but – as shown in *Figure 1.37b* – feeds 1.6mA ($I_{IL}$) into the driver when it provides a 0.4V logic-0 input. Diagram *Figure 1.37c* shows that the TTL element's output can, when in the logic-1 state, provide up to 400µA ($I_{OH}$) before its output voltage falls below 2.4V; it is thus capable of feeding up to ten Standard inputs, and is said to have a logic-1 'fan-out' (= $I_{OH}/I_{IH}$) of 10. Similarly, (d) shows that the output stage can, when in the logic-0 state, absorb up to 16 mA before its output voltage falls below 0.4V; it is thus capable of driving up to ten Standard inputs, and is said to have a logic-0 fan-out (= $I_{OL}/I_{IL}$) of 10. Thus, the element has a worst-case fan-out of 10, and it can be used to directly drive as many as ten Standard inputs.

| PARAMETER | '74'-Series TTL Sub-families | | | | | | | UNITS |
| | Standard | L | H | S | LS | AS | ALS | |
|---|---|---|---|---|---|---|---|---|
| $I_{OH}$ | 400µA | 200 | 500 | 1000 | 400 | 2000 | 400 | µA |
| $I_{IH}$ | 40µA | 10 | 50 | 50 | 20 | 20 | 20 | µA |
| Fan-out, H | 10 | 20 | 10 | 20 | 20 | 100 | 20 | – |
| $I_{OL}$ | 16mA | 2.0 | 20 | 20 | 8.0 | 20 | 8.0 | mA |
| $I_{IL}$ | 1.6mA | 0.18 | 2.0 | 2.0 | 0.36 | 0.5 | 0.2 | mA |
| Fan-out, L | 10 | 11 | 10 | 10 | 22 | 40 | 40 | – |
| Worst-case fan-out | 10 | 11 | 10 | 10 | 20 | 40 | 20 | – |

Figure 1.38   *Fan-in and fan-out values of the major TTL sub-families.*

*Figure 1.38* presents the above data in tabular form, together with similar data for all other major TTL sub-families. When working within any one sub-family, note that the most important figure here is the 'worst case fan-out (F-O)' value. Thus, if you are (for example) designing a system based entirely on LS ICs, you can confidently connect an ordinary output directly to as many as 20 normal inputs, without risk of a malfunction due to overloading (if you need to drive more than 20 inputs, you can do so via one or more high-fanout buffers, etc). Note that, *within any given sub-family,* all ordinary inputs are said (in TTL jargon) to have a fan-in of unity (1), but that in practice some MSI or LSI ICs (such as counters and registers) may have special inputs (such as Reset or Preset) with fan-in values of 2 or greater.

Sometimes, an engineer may have to mix TTL sub-families, usually so that an obsolete IC can be replaced by a readily-available

| PARAMETER | '74'-Series TTL Sub-families | | | | | | |
| | Standard | L | H | S | LS | AS | ALS |
|---|---|---|---|---|---|---|---|
| Fan-in, '1' | 1 | 0.25 | 1.25 | 1.25 | 0.5 | 0.5 | 0.5 |
| Fan-in, '0' | 1 | 0.1125 | 1.25 | 1.25 | 0.225 | 0.3125 | 0.125 |
| Fan-in, worst-case | 1 | 0.25 | 1.25 | 1.25 | 0.5 | 0.5 | 0.5 |
| Fan-out, '1' | 10 | 5 | 12.5 | 25 | 10 | 50 | 10 |
| Fan-out, '0' | 10 | 1.25 | 12.5 | 12.5 | 5 | 12.5 | 5 |
| Fan-out, worst-case | 10 | 1.25 | 12.5 | 12.5 | 5 | 12.5 | 5 |

Notes:-

Fan-in, '1' $= \dfrac{I_{IH}}{40}$ µA          Fan-out, '1' $= \dfrac{I_{OH}}{40}$ µA

Fan-in, '0' $= \dfrac{I_{IL}}{1.6}$ mA          Fan-out, '0' $= \dfrac{I_{OL}}{1.6}$ mA

Fan-in, worst-case = highest figure.          Fan-out, worst-case = lowest figure.

Figure 1.39   *TTL fan-in and fan-out in terms of 'Standard TTL' units.*

| Sub-family drivers | Sub-family inputs | | | | | | |
|---|---|---|---|---|---|---|---|
| | Standard | L | H | S | LS | AS | ALS |
| Standard TTL | 10 | 40 | 8 | 8 | 20 | 20 | 20 |
| L | 1.25 | 11 | 1 | 1 | 5.5 | 4 | 10 |
| H | 12.5 | 50 | 10 | 10 | 25 | 25 | 25 |
| S | 12.5 | 100 | 10 | 10 | 50 | 40 | 50 |
| LS | 5 | 40 | 4 | 4 | 20 | 16 | 20 |
| AS | 12.5 | 111 | 10 | 10 | 55 | 40 | 100 |
| ALS | 5 | 40 | 4 | 4 | 20 | 16 | 20 |

Note:-

$$\text{Fan-out} = \text{lowest figure of:-} \quad \frac{I_{OL}\ (driver)}{I_{IL}\ (inputs)} \quad \text{and} \quad \frac{I_{OH}\ (driver)}{I_{IH}\ (inputs)}$$

Figure 1.40 *Maximum number of TTL inputs that may be driven from any TTL sub-family output.*

modern plug-in close-equivalent. In such a case, it is necessary to relate the fan-out data of one sub-family to that of another, to check that the mix can be made without causing an input or output overload. One easy way of doing this is to simply transpose the data of *Figure 1.38* into 'Standard TTL' fan-in units, as shown in *Figure 1.39*, to gain an approximate idea of the relative 'fan' values of various sub-families. Thus, it can be seen at a glance that LS TTL has only half of the fan-in requirement of Standard TTL, but also has only half of its fan-out capability, etc.

An even more useful way of using the basic data of *Figure 1.38* is to convert it into an easily-used form that relates the fan-in and fan-out data of each TTL sub-family to all other TTL sub-families, as shown in *Figure 1.40*. Here, by reading across the left-hand columns, it can (for example) be seen that a normal LS output can drive up to 5 Standard TTL inputs, and that a Standard TTL output can safely drive up to 20 LS inputs. Thus, if an engineer is faced with a problem such as that illustrated in *Figure 1.41*, in which a fault on an old Standard TTL circuit is traced to a defective 74XXX-type IC (IC2)

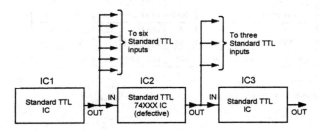

Figure 1.41 *IC2 is defective; it is a Standard TTL device. Can it be replaced directly by a 74LSXXX IC? Figure 1.40 shows that the answer is YES.*

which is used to directly drive four other Standard TTL inputs, it can be quickly seen that a 74LSXXX plug-in equivalent IC can be safely used to directly replace the IC2 Standard TTL device without incurring overload problems.

## TTL basic usage rules

The process of designing any digital electronics system can, from the design engineer's point of view, be broken down into five distinct steps. First, he or she must precisely define the problem that they are being asked to resolve. Next, they must sit down with pencil and paper and, using their intellectual abilities, generate the block diagram of a system that will resolve the problem. The third step is to translate the block diagram into a rationalized basic electronic system, using specific ICs from a logic sub-family (or sub-families) that meet the system's requirements in terms of speed, power dissipation and cost. The fourth step is a refinement of step three, and concerns checking every terminal of each individual IC, to ensure that it is used in a manner that conforms with the device's basic usage rules. The fifth and (hopefully) final step involves building an actual prototype unit and checking that it works as intended.

If the above design is based on TTL ICs, the most relevant of these design steps is, at this point in Chapter 1, that described in step four, which concerns the correct application of TTL basic usage rules. Assuming that the matter of fan-in and fan-out has already been taken care of, there are four 'basic usage' themes still outstanding, and these will now be dealt with under the headings of Power supplies, Input signals, Unused inputs, and Interfacing.

## Power supplies

'74'-series TTL ICs are designed to be used over a very limited supply voltage range (4.75V to 5.25V), and – because they generate very fast pulse edges and have relatively low noise-margin values – must be used with supplies with very low output impedance values (typically less than 0.1 ohms). Consequently, practical TTL circuits should always be powered from a low-impedance well-regulated supply such as one of those shown in *Figures 1.42* to *1.44*, and must be used with a PCB that is very carefully designed to give excellent

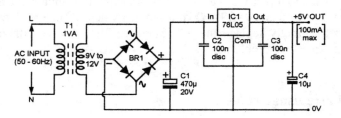

Figure 1.42  *5V regulated DC supply (100mA maximum output).*

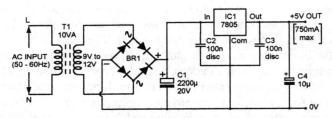

Figure 1.43  *5V regulated DC supply (750mA maximum output).*

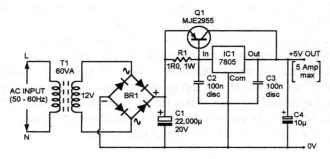

Figure 1.44  *5V regulated DC supply (5A maximum output).*

high-frequency supply decoupling to each TTL IC. In general, the PCB's +5V and 0V supply rail tracks must be as wide as possible (ideally, the '0V' track should take the form of a ground plane), all connections and inter-connections should be as short and direct as possible, the PCB's supply rails should be liberally sprinkled with 4.7µF Tantalum electrolytic capacitors (at least one per 10 ICs) to enhance l.f. decoupling, and with 10nF disk ceramics (at least one per 4 ICs, fitted as close as possible between an IC's supply pins) to enhance h.f. decoupling.

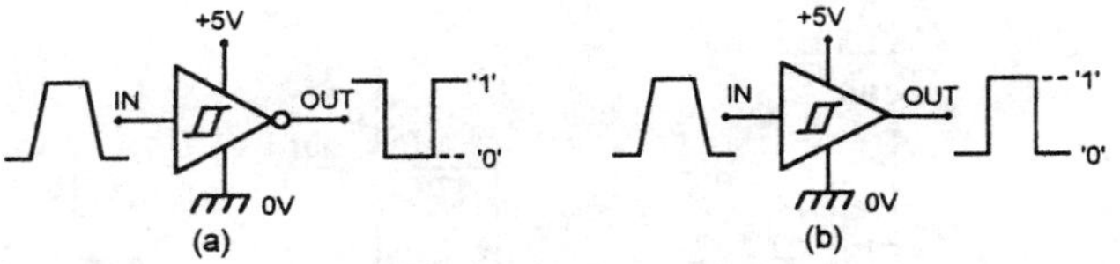

Figure 1.45 *'Slow' input signals can be converted into fast ones via (a) an inverting or (b) non-inverting Schmitt element.*

## Input signals

When using TTL, all IC input signals must – unless the IC is fitted with a Schmitt-type input – have very sharp rising and falling edges (typical rise and fall times should be less than 40ns on LS TTL, for example). If rise or fall times are too long, they may allow the input terminal to hover in the TTL element's linear 'indeterminate' zone (see *Figures 1.33* and *1.35*) long enough for the element to burst into wild oscillations and generate spasmodic output signals that may disrupt associated circuitry (such as counters and registers, for example). If necessary, 'slow' input signals can be converted into 'fast' ones by feeding them to the IC's input terminal via an inverting or non-inverting Schmitt element, as shown in *Figure 1.45*.

## Unused inputs

Unused TTL input terminals should never be allowed to simply 'float', since this makes them susceptible to noise pick-up, etc. Instead, they should be tied to definite logic levels, either by connecting them to $V_{CC}$ via a 1k0 resistor, or shorting them directly to the ground rail, or by connecting them to a TTL input or output terminal that is already in use. *Figure 1.46* shows examples of the four options. The simplest option is to tie the unused input to $V_{CC}$ via a 1k0 resistor, as shown in *Figure 1.46a*; this resistor has to supply only a few µA of current ($I_{IH}$) to each input, and can thus easily drive up to 10 unwanted inputs. Alternatively, the input can be tied directly to ground, as in *Figure 1.46b*, but in this case an input current of several hundred µA ($I_{IL}$) may flow to the ground rail via the input.

If the unwanted input is on a multi-input gate, it can be disabled by shorting it to one of the gate's used inputs, as in *Figure 1.46c*, where a 3-input AND gate is shown used as a 2-input type. If the IC is a multiple gate-type in which an entire gate is unwanted, the gate should be disabled by tying its inputs high if it is a non-inverting

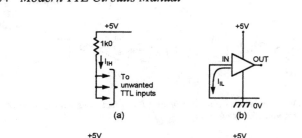

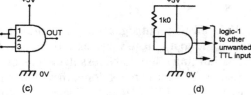

Figure 1.46  *Alternative ways of connecting unwanted TTL inputs (see text).*

(AND or OR) type, or shorting them to ground if it is an inverting (NAND or NOR) type; if desired, the output of this gate can then be used as a fixed logic-1 point that can be used to drive other unwanted inputs, as shown in *Figure 1.46d.*

## Interfacing

An interface circuit is one that enables one type of system to be sensibly connected to a different type of system. In a purely TTL system, in which all ICs are designed to connect directly together, interface circuitry is usually needed only at the system's initial input and final output points, to enable them to merge with the outside world via items such as switches, sensors, relays, indicators, etc. Occasionally, however, TTL ICs may be used in conjunction with other logic families (such as CMOS), in which case an interface may be needed between the different families. Thus, as far as TTL is concerned, there are three basic classes of interface circuit, which will now be dealt with under the headings of Input interfacing, Output interfacing, and Logic family interfacing.

### Input interfacing

Basically, the digital signals arriving at the inputs of any TTL system must be 'clean' ones with TTL-defined logic-0 and logic-1 levels

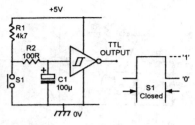

Figure 1.47  *Switch-debouncing input interface.*

and with very fast rise and fall times (less than 40ns in LS TTL systems). It is the task of input interfacing circuitry to convert external input signals into this format. *Figures 1.47* to *1.50* show a few simple examples of such circuitry.

Mechanically-derived switching signals are notoriously 'bouncy' (see *Figure 1.11*) and must be cleaned up before being fed to a normal TTL input. *Figure 1.47* shows a practical switch-debouncing input interfacing circuit; here, C1 charges – with a time constant of about 10ms – via R1-R2 when S1 is open and generates a logic-0 output via the TTL Schmitt inverter; when S1 is closed it rapidly discharges C1 via R2, driving the Schmitt output high; the effects of any switch-generated 'bounce' signals are eliminated by the circuit's 10 mS time constant, and a clean TTL switching waveform is thus available at the Schmitt's output.

*Figure 1.48* shows a circuit that can be used to interface almost any clean digital signal to a normal TTL input. Here, when the input signal is below 500mV (Q1's minimum turn-on voltage), Q1 is cut off and the inverting Schmitt TTL output is at logic-0; when the input is significantly above 600mV, Q1 is driven on and the Schmitt output goes to logic-1. Note that the digital input signal can have any maximum voltage value, and R1 is chosen to simply limit Q1's base current to a safe value.

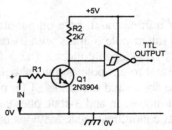

Figure 1.48  *Transistor input interface.*

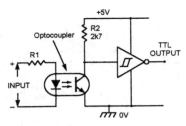

Figure 1.49  *Optocoupler input interface.*

*Figure 1.49* is a simple variation of the above circuit, with the transistor built into an optocoupler; the circuit action is such that the
Schmitt's output is at logic-0 when the optocoupler input is zero, and
at logic-1 when the input is high; note that the optocoupler provides
total electrical isolation between the input and TTL signals.

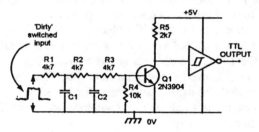

Figure 1.50  *'Dirty-switching' input interface.*

Finally, *Figure 1.50* is another simple circuit variation, with the
basic digital input signal fed to Q1's base via the R1–C1–R2–C2
low-pass filter network, which eliminates unwanted high-frequency components and thus can convert very 'dirty' input signals (such as those
from vehicle contact-breakers, for example) into a clean TTL format.

## Output interfacing

Most TTL ICs have normal totem-pole output stages, but some of
them have modified totem-pole outputs with 3-state (Tri-State) gating; a few TTL ICs have open-collector (o.c.) totem-pole output
stages. Note that normal totem-pole outputs should not (except in a
few special cases) be connected in parallel. TTL o.c. outputs *can* be
connected in parallel, however, and 3-state ones can be connected in
parallel under special conditions; basic methods of using o.c. and 3-
state outputs are described in Chapter 2.

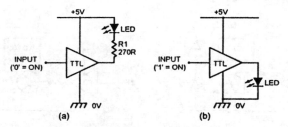

Figure 1.51 *LED-driving output interfaces, using non-inverting TTL elements*

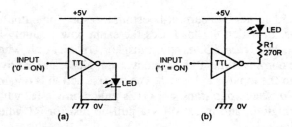

Figure 1.52 *LED-driving output interfaces, using inverting TTL elements.*

A normal totem-pole output stage can source or sink useful amounts of output current, and can be used in a variety of ways to interface with the outside world. A few simple examples of such circuits are shown in *Figures 1.51* to *1.58*. *Figure 1.51* shows a couple of ways of driving LED output indicators via non-inverting TTL elements. Note that a normal TTL output can sink fairly high load currents (typically up to 50mA in an LS device), but has an internally-limited output sourcing ability; thus, the LED current must be limited to a safe value via R1 if it is connected as in *Figure 1.51a*, but is internally limited in *Figure 1.51b*. *Figure 1.52* shows alternative ways of driving LEDs, using inverting TTL elements.

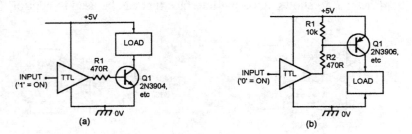

Figure 1.53 *Current-boosting load-driving output interfaces.*

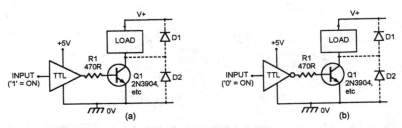

Figure 1.54  *Output interface to load with independent positive rail.*

*Figure 1.53* shows two current-boosting load-driving output interface circuits, in which the load uses the same power supply as the TTL circuit. In *Figure 1.53a*, npn transistor Q1 is cut off when the input of the non-inverting TTL element is at logic-0, and is driven on via R1 when the input is at logic-1. The reverse action is obtained in *Figure 1.53b*, where pnp transistor Q1 is pulled on via R2 when the input is at logic-0, and is cut off via pull-up resistor R1 when the input is at logic-1.

*Figure 1.54* shows two output interface circuits that can be used to drive loads that use independent positive supply rails. Q1 is turned on by a logic-1 input in *Figure 1.54a*, and a logic-0 input in *Figure 1.54b*. If the external load is inductive (such as a relay or motor), the circuits should be fitted with protection diodes, as shown dotted in the diagrams.

*Figure 1.55* shows two optocoupled output interface circuits that can be used to drive loads that use fully independent DC power supplies; the load is turned on via a logic-1 input in *Figure 1.55a*, and a logic-0 input in *Figure 1.55b*. Note that the optocoupler input (the LED) could alternatively be connected between the +5V rail and the TTL output via a current-limiting resistor, using the same basic connections as *Figure 1.51a* or *Figure 1.52b*.

*Figure 1.56* shows an output interface that can be used to control

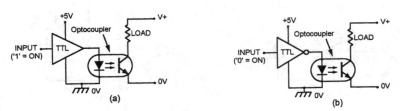

Figure 1.55  *Optocoupled output interface.*

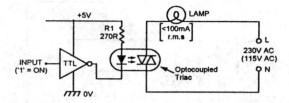

Figure 1.56 *Output interface to a low-power AC lamp via an optocoupled triac.*

a low-power lamp or similar resistive load that is driven from AC power lines and consumes no more than about 100mA of current. This circuit uses an optocoupled triac, and these typically need a LED input current of less than 15mA and can handle triac load currents of up to about 100mA mean (500mA surge) at up to 400V peak. Note that optocoupled triacs are best used to activate a high-power 'slave' triac, that can drive a load of any desired power rating. *Figures 1.57* and *1.58* show two such circuits.

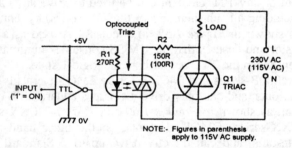

Figure 1.57 *Output interface to a high-power non-inductive AC load.*

The circuit in *Figure 1.57* is suitable for use with non-inductive loads such as lamps and heating elements. It can be modified for use with inductive loads such as motors by using the connections of *Figure 1.58*, in which R2–C1–R3 provide a degree of phase-shift to the triac gate-drive network, to ensure correct triac triggering action, and R4–C2 form a snubber network, to suppress rate effects.

## Logic family interfacing

It is generally bad practice to mix different logic families in any system, but on those occasions where it does occur the mix is usually made between TTL and CMOS devices that share a common 5V power supply; in this case the form or necessity of any interfacing circuitry depends on the direction of the interface and on the precise

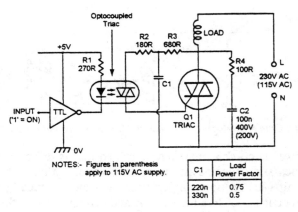

Figure 1.58   *Output interface to a high-power inductive load.*

sub-families that are involved; *Figures 1.59* to *1.62* show the four most useful types of interface arrangement.

The output of any TTL element can be used to drive any CMOS logic IC (including all sub-members of the '74' series) by using the connections shown in *Figure 1.59*, in which R1 is used as a TTL pull-up resistor and ensures that the CMOS consumes minimal quiescent current when the TTL output is in the logic-1 state.

Standard 4000B-series and 74CXX-series CMOS elements have very low fan-outs, and can only drive a single Standard TTL or LS TTL element, as shown in *Figures 1.60* and *1.61*. 74HCXX-series (and 74ACXX-series) CMOS elements, on the other hand, have excellent fan-outs, and can directly drive up to 2 Standard TTL inputs, or 10 LS TTL inputs, or 20 ALS TTL inputs, as shown in *Figure 1.62*.

In cases where the TTL and CMOS ICs use individual positive supply rails (5V for TTL, 3V to 18V for CMOS), an interface can be made between the two systems by using a direct-coupled npn tran-

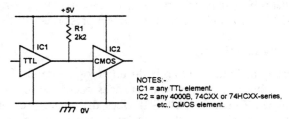

Figure 1.59   *TTL-to-CMOS interface.*

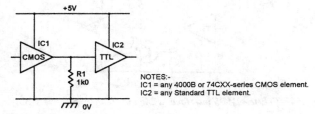

Figure 1.60 *CMOS-to-Standard-TTL interface.*

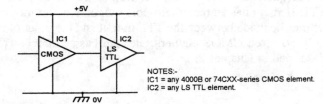

Figure 1.61 *CMOS-to-LS-TTL interface.*

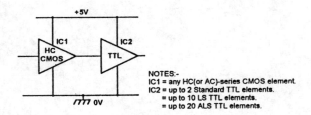

Figure 1.62 *HC-CMOS-to-TTL interface.*

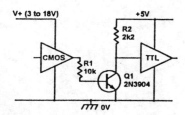

Figure 1.63 *CMOS-to-TTL interface, using independent positive supply rails.*

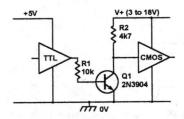

**Figure 1.64** *TTL-to-CMOS interface, using independent positive supply rails.*

sistor as a level-shifter between them, as shown in *Figures 1.63* and *1.64* (these simple circuits may need some refining if they are to be used at frequencies above a few hundred kHz). Finally, note that if the TTL element has an o.c. totem-pole output, a direct interface can sometimes be made between the TTL output and the input of an individually-powered CMOS element, etc; the basics of this technique are described in Chapter 2.

# 2 TTL buffer, gate and logic circuits

Buffers, inverters and gates are the most basic elements used in modern digital electronics, and are available in many variations in TTL. The eight best-known logic gates are the buffer and the NOT, OR, NOR, AND, NAND, EX-OR and EX-NOR types. Comprehensive details of these and various other types of TTL logic are given in this chapter, which starts off by looking at logic gate symbology and then goes on to briefly investigate mathematical aspects of digital logic before finally getting down to the nitty-gritty of practical TTL gate and logic circuitry.

## Logic gate symbology

Many different symbols can be used to represent each of the eight basic logic gate elements. *Figure 2.1* shows four different families of symbols that are widely used in various parts of the world today; of these, the American MIL/ANSI symbols are by far the most popular, are instantly recognizable, are used by most practical digital engineers throughout the world, and are used exclusively throughout the rest of this volume. Two useful variations of these American symbols are also used in this book, and these are shown added to a standard inverter symbol in *Figure 2.2*; the left-hand symbol is internationally recognised and indicates that the logic element has a Schmitt-trigger input action; the right-hand symbol – which is widely used but is not universally recognized – indicates that the logic element has an open-collector (o.c.) totem-pole output stage.

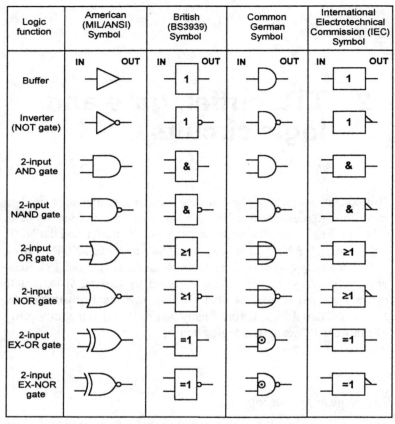

| Logic function | American (MIL/ANSI) Symbol | British (BS3939) Symbol | Common German Symbol | International Electrotechnical Commission (IEC) Symbol |
|---|---|---|---|---|
| Buffer | | 1 | | 1 |
| Inverter (NOT gate) | | 1 | | 1 |
| 2-input AND gate | | & | | & |
| 2-input NAND gate | | & | | & |
| 2-input OR gate | | ≥1 | | ≥1 |
| 2-input NOR gate | | ≥1 | | ≥1 |
| 2-input EX-OR gate | | =1 | | =1 |
| 2-input EX-NOR gate | | =1 | | =1 |

Figure 2.1   *A selection of widely used logic symbols.*

Schmitt inverter

Inverter with o.c.
(open collector) output

Figure 2.2   *Useful variations of the MIL/ANSI inverter symbol.*

## Logic gate functions

The functional action of any logic gate can be presented or represented in either a descriptive, tabular or symbolic way. The following list presents the functions of all eight basic types of gate in purely descriptive terms:

*Buffers.* A buffer is simply a non-inverting amplifier that has an output drive capacity that is far greater than its input drive requirement, i.e., it has a high fan-out and gives a logic-1 output for a logic-1 input, etc.

*Inverters.* An inverter is an amplifier with a high fan-out, and gives a logic-1 output for a logic-0 input, and vice versa; in inverter may also be known as a NOT gate.

*AND gates.* An AND gate has an output that is normally at logic-0 and only goes to logic-1 when ALL inputs are at logic-1, i.e., when inputs A and B and C, etc., are high.

*NAND gates.* A NAND gate is an AND gate with a negated (inverted) output; it has an output that is normally at logic-1 and only goes to logic-0 when ALL inputs are at logic-1.

*OR gates.* An OR gate has an output that goes to logic-1 if ANY input is at logic-1, i.e., if inputs A or B or C, etc., are high. Note that the output goes to logic-0 only if ALL inputs are at logic-0.

*NOR gates.* A NOR gate is an OR gate with a negated output; it has an output that goes to logic-0 if any input is at logic-1, and goes to logic-1 only when ALL inputs are at logic-0.

*EX-OR gates.* Exclusive-OR (EX-OR) gates have two inputs, and their output goes to logic-1 only if a SINGLE input (A *or* B) is at logic-1; the output goes to logic-0 if BOTH inputs are in the same logic state.

*EX-NOR gates.* An Exclusive-NOR (EX-NOR) gate is an EX-OR gate with a negated output, which goes to logic-1 if BOTH inputs are in the same logic state, and goes to logic-0 only if a single input is at logic-1.

*Figure 2.3* shows how the functions of these eight gates can also be presented in tabular form, via Truth Tables (which show the logic state of the output at all possible combinations of input logic states), or symbolically, in Boolean algebraic terms. Note when representing logic gate functions that, by convention, all inputs are notated alphabetically as 'A', 'B', 'C', etc., and the output terminal is always notated as 'Y' (but in counters and flip-flops, etc., the main output is

| Logic function | Logic symbol | Truth table | Boolean expression |
|---|---|---|---|
| Buffer |  A ▷ Y | A Y<br>0 0<br>1 1 | $Y = A$ |
| Inverter (NOT gate) | 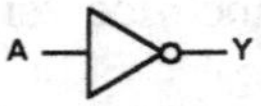 A ▷○ Y | A Y<br>0 1<br>1 0 | $Y = \overline{A}$ |
| 2-input AND gate |  A, B ⟶ Y | A B Y<br>0 0 0<br>0 1 0<br>1 0 0<br>1 1 1 | $Y = A \cdot B$ |
| 2-input NAND gate | 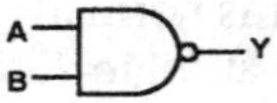 A, B ⟶ Y | A B Y<br>0 0 1<br>0 1 1<br>1 0 1<br>1 1 0 | $Y = \overline{A \cdot B}$ |
| 2-input OR gate |  A, B ⟶ Y | A B Y<br>0 0 0<br>0 1 1<br>1 0 1<br>1 1 1 | $Y = A + B$ |
| 2-input NOR gate | 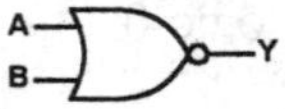 A, B ⟶ Y | A B Y<br>0 0 1<br>0 1 0<br>1 0 0<br>1 1 0 | $Y = \overline{A + B}$ |
| 2-input EX-OR gate |  A, B ⟶ Y | A B Y<br>0 0 0<br>0 1 1<br>1 0 1<br>1 1 0 | $Y = A \oplus B$ |
| 2-input EX-NOR gate | 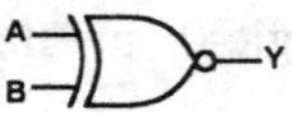 A, B ⟶ Y | A B Y<br>0 0 1<br>0 1 0<br>1 0 0<br>1 1 1 | $Y = \overline{A \oplus B}$ |

Figure 2.3   *Symbols, Truth Tables, and Boolean expressions for the eight basic types of logic gate.*

usually notated as 'Q'). The actual logic states may be represented by '0' and '1', as shown, or by 'L' (= Low logic level) and 'H' (= High logic level).

Regarding the Boolean expressions in *Figure 2.3*, if you are not already familiar with this algebraic form of expression the following brief notes may aid your understanding of the subject.

## Boolean algebra basics

Boolean algebra is a fairly old (1854) branch of mathematics, and was devised to help resolve philosophical problems concerning logic and probability, in which – in essence – a number of 'inputs' each have only two possible states ('yes' or 'no', 'true' or 'false', etc.), and combine to produce a final output that also has only two possible states ('yes' or 'no', etc). It was specifically devised to resolve what are, in essence, purely binary (two-state) logic problems, and has subsequently proved to be a useful tool in the field of modern digital electronics.

Unfortunately, much Boolean symbology is based on 'pure logic' (rather than normal common sense) concepts, and coincidentally conflicts with some of the symbology used in modern electronics; these facts sometimes tend to hinder the newcomer's understanding of the subject. Consequently, to begin understanding Boolean algebra *in the context of modern digital electronics*, you must first clear your mind of all conventional notions concerning the use of signs such as '=', '+', '.', etc., and realize that they are in fact mere man-derived symbols that can be used to represent anything you wish. Specifically, note the following points.

In Boolean algebra, in the context of modern digital electronics, logic gate inputs and outputs are notated in the alphabetic manner shown in *Figure 2.3*, and it is implicit that – unless otherwise indicated – the notated terminal is in a logic-1 state. Thus, in the case of the *Figure 2.3* buffer, the simple Boolean statement 'A' (or 'Y') actually means 'input A (or output Y) is in a logic-1 state'. If the notated terminal is NOT in the logic-1 state, it obviously must be in the logic-0 state, and this fact is notated in Boolean symbology by a negation bar drawn above the basic symbol. Thus, the simple statement '$\bar{A}$' (pronounced *not*-A) actually means 'input A is in a logic-0 state'.

In Boolean algebra, the sign '=' is pronounced *equals*, but actually means 'when'. Thus, the buffer expression '$Y = A$' is read as '$Y$ *equals* $A$' but actually means 'output Y is in a logic-1 state *when* input A is in a logic-1 state'. Similarly, the inverter expression '$Y =$

$\bar{A}$' is read as '*Y equals not-A*' but means 'output Y is in a logic-1 state *when* input A is in a logic-0 state'.

In Boolean algebra, the dot sign (.) indicates a logical-AND function, a plus sign (+) indicates a logical-OR function, and a circled plus sign (+J49) indicates an Exclusive-OR (EX-OR) function. Thus, in *Figure 2.3*, the 2-input AND gate expression 'Y = A.B' reads as '*Y equals A AND B*' but means 'output Y is in a logic-1 state *when* inputs A AND B are in a logic-1 state', and so on. Note that, in practice, Boolean rules allow the dot (AND) sign to be omitted between input symbols, its presence being implicit unless otherwise notated (by a + sign, etc.); thus, the expression 'ABC' has the same meaning as 'A.B.C' or 'A AND B AND C'.

Note in the NAND, NOR and EX-NOR Boolean expressions that all the right-hand symbols – including the logic signs – are negated by a single bar, and that a negated AND becomes an OR, and a negated OR becomes an AND. Thus, the Boolean 2-input NAND gate expression in *Figure 2.3* means 'output Y is in a logic-1 state *when* input A OR B is in a logic-0 state'. When an EX-OR is negated it becomes an AND, but the logic states of A and B are unimportant as long as they are both the SAME. Thus, the 2-input EX-NOR gate exression means 'output Y is in a logic-1 state *when* inputs A AND B are both in the SAME state'. In practice, when dealing with fully negated expressions such as these it is sometimes best to remember

A (or B) *means* "input A (or B) is at logic-1".

$\bar{A}$ (not-A) *means* "input A is at logic-0".

Y *means* "output Y is at logic-1".

Equals (=) *means* "when".

Dot (• or . ) *means* logical AND.

Plus (+) *means* logical OR.

Circled plus ($\oplus$) *means* logical EX-OR.

A.B.C *has the same meaning as* ABC.

ABC *has the same meaning as* A AND B AND C.

A negated AND ($\overline{AND}$) *has the same meaning as* OR.

A negated OR ($\overline{OR}$) *has the same meaning as* AND.

'Y = $\overline{A.B}$' *has the same meaning as* '$\bar{Y}$ = A.B'.

'Y = $\overline{A+B}$' *has the same meaning as* '$\bar{Y}$ = A+B'.

Figure 2.4  *Meanings of Boolean symbols, within the context of modern digital electronics.*

| | |
|---|---|
| Absorbtion laws: | $A+(A.B) = A$ <br> $A.(A+B) = A$ |
| Annulment laws: | $A+1 = 1$ <br> $A.0 = 0$ |
| Associative laws: | $(A+B)+C = A+(B+C) = A+B+C$ <br> $(A.B).C = A.(B.C) = A.B.C$ |
| Commutative laws: | $A+B = B+A$ <br> $A.B = B.A$ |
| Complementation laws: | $A+\bar{A} = 1$ <br> $A.\bar{A} = 0$ |
| Distributive laws: | $A.(B+C) = (A.B)+(A.C)$ <br> $A+(B.C) = (A+B).(A+C)$ <br> $(A+B).(A+C).(A+D) = A+(B.C.D)$ |
| Double negation: | $\text{not } \bar{A} = \bar{\bar{A}} = A$ |
| Expansion laws: | $(A+B).(A+\bar{B}) = A$ <br> $(A.B)+(A.\bar{B}) = A$ |
| Identity: | $A+0 = A$ <br> $A.1 = A$ |
| De Morgan's rule 1: | $\overline{A+B} = \bar{A}.\bar{B}$ |
| De Morgan's rule 2: | $\overline{A.B} = \bar{A}+\bar{B}$ |
| Tautology laws: | $A.A = A$ <br> $A+A = A$ |

Figure 2.5 *Some basic laws of Boolean algebra.*

that they are equivalent to a statement in which only the Y sign is negated, and to thus mentally shift the negation bar to the left-hand (Y) side of the equation; the NOR expression then means 'output Y is in a logic-0 state *when* inputs A OR B are in a logic-1 state'.

## Boolean algebra rules/laws

*Figure 2.4* lists the most important of the above Boolean symbol meanings and basic Boolean rules, as they apply in the context of modern digital electronics, and *Figure 2.5* lists the most-often-quoted 'laws' of Boolean algebra, some of which seem staggeringly self-evident. The *double negation* law, for example, effectively states that when A is NOT a not-A it is an A, and the first *annulment* law effectively states that A (which is a logic-1) OR logic-1 equals logic-1, etc.

*Figure 2.6* shows a practical example of how sensible application of Boolean algebra can be a real help in solving a logic design problem. Suppose here that you are asked to design a 3-input logic

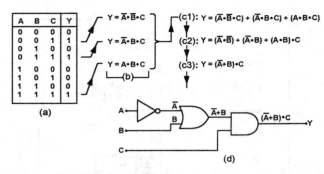

(a)

(d)

**Figure 2.6**   *Example of the use of Boolean algebra to help solve a problem in logic gate design (see text).*

system that will comply with the conditions laid down in the Truth Table *(Figure 2.6a)*, in which the Y output goes to logic-1 under the three specified alternative sets of input conditions. Your first design step is to draw up a Boolean expression for each of the three sets of 'Y' conditions, as in *(Figure 2.6b)*, and then to convert this into a single expression, as in *Figure 2.6c (1)*, where each of the three sets of AND conditions are enclosed in brackets and joined by OR signs. The next step is to progressively reduce this expression to a minimized form – using common sense and various basic Boolean laws – first as in *Figure 2.6c (2)*, and finally as in Figure 2.6c (3). From *Figure 2.6c* (3), note that your logic system must invert input A, OR it with B, and AND the result with C; this obviously calls for the use of a gate that, in essence, consists of a NOT, OR and AND gate inter-connected as shown in *Figure 2.6d*. In practice, it is usually best to construct these gates from Quad 2-input NOR or NAND ICs, as described later in this chapter.

Note in *Figure 2.6d* that, if you are presented with a gate diagram,

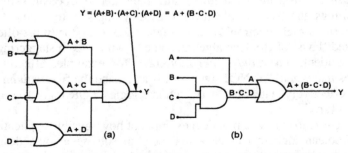

**Figure 2.7**   *Example of the use of Boolean algebra to help simplify a gate design.*

it is fairly easy to work out the gate's Boolean expression by tracing the input paths through the individual gate elements, as shown. Thus, if you are presented with the gate diagram of *Figure 2.7a* you will probably quickly work out its Boolean expression as shown and almost instantly realise (from the third *Distributive law* of *Figure 2.5*) that it can be minimized to the expression Y = A + (B.C.D), which itself implies that the same logic result can be obtained from one 2-input OR gate and a 3-input AND gate connected as shown in the simple circuit of *Figure 2.7b*.

## Positive versus Negative logic

All modern TTL circuitry assumes the use of the 'Positive logic' convention, in which a logic-1 state is High and a logic-0 state is Low. In the early days of electronic digital circuitry an alternative 'Negative logic' convention – in which a logic-1 state is Low and a logic-0 state is High – was also in common use, and it is sometimes still useful to be able to think in Negative-logic terms, particularly when designing gates in which a Low-state output is of special interest. With this point in mind, *Figure 2.8* presents a basic set of 2-input Positive and Negative logic equivalents. Thus, it can be seen that a Negative logic AND gate action – in which the output is Low only when both inputs are Low – is directly available from a Positive logic OR gate, and so on.

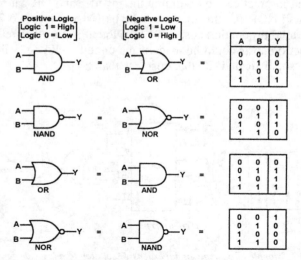

Figure 2.8 *Basic set of 2-input Positive and Negative logic equivalents.*

## Practical logic-gate design

In the early days of digital electronics, design engineers used to make much use of Boolean algebra and a technique known as Karnaugh mapping when trying to develop logic-gate systems that could be produced at absolute minimum cost. The advent of the '74' series of TTL logic ICs changed that situation dramatically, partly because most of the 'gate' ICs in this range have lots of built-in spare capacity or 'redundancy'. Most 2-input gates, for example, are only available in 'Quad' packages, and 3-input gates are available in 'Triple' packages; thus, the theoretically superior logic circuit of *Figure 2.7b* in fact has no practical advantage over that of *Figure 2.7a* (unless some genuine use can be found for the two saved OR gates), since both designs call for the use of one Quad and one Triple IC.

In the early days of the '74' series, digital ICs were fairly expensive, and formed a significant part of the total cost of producing a printed circuit assembly. Today, most digital ICs are very cheap, and cost only a small part of the total price of producing a PCB assembly. Take, for example, the cost of producing the circuit in *Figure 2.6*, in rough 'dollars and cents' terms, as part of an existing short-run assembly. If this circuit is built exactly as drawn, it needs three ICs, costing 25 cents each, and each costing 50 cents to assemble and test on the PCB; it thus costs a total of $2.25 to build. But in practice – by building the inverter and OR gate from a single quad NOR IC, the circuit can be built using just two 25-cent ICs, at a total production cost of $1.50. Note that a further reduction in production costs could be made if the circuit could be built using a single 'sophisticated' IC that cost less than $1.00.

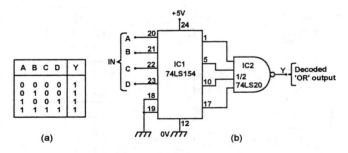

Figure 2.9 *Example of a simple and inexpensive solution to a logic design problem (see text).*

Clearly, then, the practical electronics engineer must keep firmly in touch with the economic realities of cost-effective design. When designing circuits for large-scale production, he or she must strive to minimize IC counts rather than IC costs, and when designing one-off or short-run circuits must always strive to minimize actual design times and costs. In general, when designing logic systems, it is rarely worthwhile basing the design on SSI logic ICs (such as simple gates, for example) if total design time is likely to exceed one hour, or if more than two ICs are needed to implement the basic logic function or functions. The use of Boolean algebra, etc., is thus now confined to fairly simple design problems.

*Figure 2.9* shows a practical example of a quick and cost-effective solution to an apparently difficult logic design problem, in which a circuit is required to give a logic-1 output on 'Y' when inputs A to D have any one of the four 4-bit logic-state combinations shown in *Figure 2.9a*. A mere glance shows that a suitable logic network can be built using four 25-cent SSI ICs (a Hex inverter, two Dual 4-input AND gates, and one 4-input OR gate, connected as shown in *Figure 2.30*), and this involves a building cost of $3.00 ($1.00 for parts, and $2.00 for assembly).

The cheaper alternative is shown in *Figure 2.9b*; it uses a $1.00 24-pin MSI 74LS154 4-line to 16-line decoder IC (see Chapter 7 for details), which decodes all sixteen possible 4-bit input combinations and presents each of them – one at a time – to its own output terminal as a logic-0, while the other fifteen outputs remain at logic-1. In this circuit, the four desired outputs (from pins 1, 5, 10 and 17) are effectively ORed and inverted via half of a 25-cent 74LS20 dual 4-input NAND gate and passed on to 'Y', which thus goes to logic-1 whenever one of the desired 4-bit inputs is present. Thus, this two-IC circuit costs only $2.25 to build ($1.25 for parts and $1.00 for assembly) and can be designed in just a few minutes, without the need to resort to time-consuming calculation in Boolean algebra or Karnaugh mapping, etc.

## Practical TTL buffer circuits

So far in this chapter, gates have been treated as purely abstract devices. It is time now to move on and look at them in practical TTL form, starting off with buffer ICs.

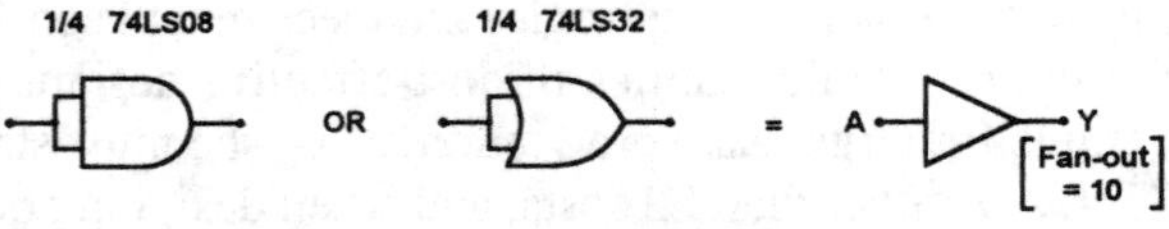

1/4  74LS08                1/4  74LS32

OR                    = A ▷ Y
                              [Fan-out = 10]

Figure 2.10  *Any AND or OR gate can be used as a non-inverting buffer element.*

1/3 74LS04                           1/3 74LS14

= A ▷ Y                              = A ▷ Y
     [Fan-out = 10]                       [Fan-out = 10]

(a)                                  (b)

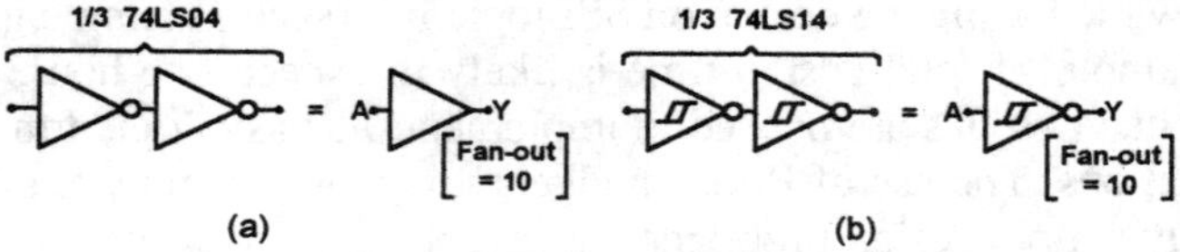

Figure 2.11  *Any two elements from a Hex inverter IC can be used to make a non-inverting buffer element.*

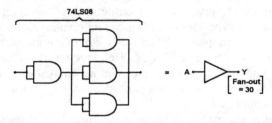

74LS08

= A ▷ Y
     [Fan-out = 30]

Figure 2.12  *A Quad AND gate IC used as a non-inverting buffer with a fan-out of 30.*

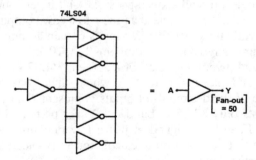

74LS04

= A ▷ Y
     [Fan-out = 50]

Figure 2.13  *A Hex inverter IC used as a non-inverting buffer with a fan-out of 50.*

Modern TTL buffer ICs have two main purposes, and these are either to act as simple non-inverting current- or voltage-boosting interfaces between one part of a circuit and another, or to act as 3-state switching units that can be used to connect a circuit's outputs to a common bus only when required. Note when selecting ICs for use in these applications that an IC's price is set more by its sales volume than by its circuit complexity, and that the simplest gate ICs are not

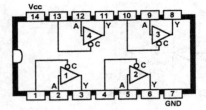

| C | A | Y | Is (per gate) |
|---|---|---|---|
| 0 | 0 | 0 | 2.25mA |
| 0 | 1 | 1 | 1.12mA |
| 1 | 0 | Hi-Z | 2.75mA |
| 1 | 1 | Hi-Z | 2.62mA |

Note: Normal fan-out = 30

Figure 2.14 *Functional diagram and Truth Table, etc., of the 74LS125 Quad 3-state buffer/bus-driver IC.*

necessarily the cheapest. Also note that if you merely need a few buffers with fan-outs of 10, one cheap way to get them is to make them from quad AND or OR ICs, as shown in *Figure 2.10*, or from normal or Schmitt Hex inverters, as shown in *Figure 2.11*. You can also use these ICs to make buffers with fan-out values greater than 10 by using the techniques shown in *Figures 2.12* and *2.13*, in which a number of logic elements *from within the same IC package* are wired in parallel and driven from a single source, so that their fan-out values are effectively added together. Thus, the circuits in *Figures 2.12* and *2.13* have fan-out values of 30 and 50 respectively.

If you need a few buffers with fan-outs of 30, one cheap way to get them is to use a 74LS125 Quad 3-state buffer IC. *Figure 2.14* shows the functional diagram and Truth Table, etc., of this device, which is housed in a 14-pin package and is so modestly priced that it is still worth using even if you do not need the '3-state' facility. Note from the Truth Table that each of the four elements acts as a normal buffer when its control terminal (C) is in the logic-0 state, and that each element's quiescent supply current ($I_s$) is least when C is at logic-0 and the buffer's input (A) is at logic-1. Thus, any unwanted elements should be disabled by tying their C terminals Low and their A terminals High, using one of the methods shown in *Figure 2.15*, and any element can be used as a normal buffer by grounding its C terminal as in *Figure 2.16*, or as a 3-state buffer that drives a common bus line by using it as shown in *Figure 2.17*.

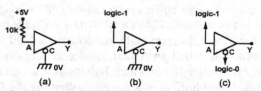

Figure 2.15 *All unwanted 74LS125 elements must be connected in one of these ways.*

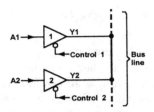

Figure 2.16   *Method of using a 74LS125 element as a normal buffer.*

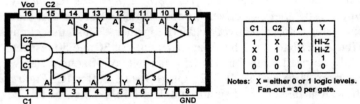

Figure 2.17   *Method of using a 74LS125 element as a 3-state line-driving buffer.*

| C1 | C2 | A | Y |
|----|----|----|----|
| 1 | X | X | HI-Z |
| X | 1 | X | HI-Z |
| 0 | 0 | 1 | 1 |
| 0 | 0 | 0 | 0 |

Notes:  X = either 0 or 1 logic levels.
Fan-out = 30 per gate.

Figure 2.18   *Functional diagram and Truth Table of the 74LS365 Hex 3-state buffer.*

If you need five or six buffers with fan-outs of 30, one of the cheapest ways to get them is to use a 74LS365 Hex 3-state buffer IC. *Figure 2.18* shows the functional diagram and basic Truth Table of this 16-pin IC; note that all six buffers share a common AND-gated control line. Thus, the IC can be used as six normal buffers by grounding its two control pins as shown in *Figure 2.19*, or as a set of six 3-state buffers that are all switched via one common control signal as shown in *Figure 2.20*; AND-type 3-state control can be obtained by using both 'Control' terminals (pins 1 and 15).

If you need seven or eight buffers with fan-outs of 30, one cheap way to get them is to use a 74LS244 Octal 3-state buffer IC. *Figure 2.21* shows the functional diagram and basic Truth Table of this 20-pin IC, which although called an 'Octal' device is actually a dual Quad 3-state Schmitt buffer IC, in which buffers 1–4 are controlled via the CA terminal, and buffers 5–8 are controlled via the CB terminal. Each of these Quads can be used as a set of simple Schmitt

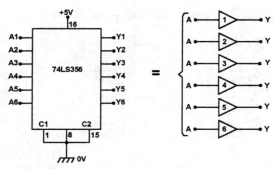

Figure 2.19 *Method of connecting the 74LS356 for use as six normal buffers.*

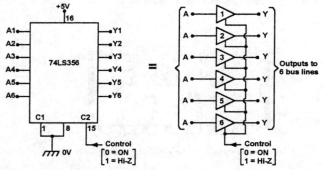

Figure 2.20 *Method of connecting the 74LS356 for use as a 3-state Hex buffer controlled via a single input.*

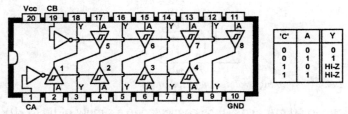

Figure 2.21 *Functional diagram and Truth Table of the 74LS244 Octal (dual Quad) 3-state Schmitt buffer IC.*

buffers by grounding its control terminal as shown in *Figure 2.22a*, or as a ganged set of 3-state Schmitt buffers by using its Control terminal as shown in *Figure 2.22b*.

To complete this look at TTL buffers, *Figure 2.23* shows the functional diagram of the 7407 Standard-TTL Hex buffer IC; each of these buffers has an open-collector (o.c.) totem-pole output that can

Note. Figures in parenthesis ( ) apply to the 5-to-8 set of buffers.

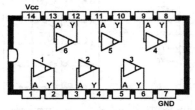

Figure 2.22   *The 74LS244 'Quad v.' buffers can be used as (a) simple Schmitt buffers, or as (b) 3-state ganged Schmitt buffers.*

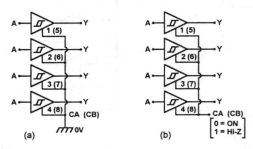

Figure 2.23   *Functional diagram of the 7407 Hex buffer with 30V o.c. outputs.*

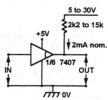

Figure 2.24   *5V to high-voltage buffer/interface.*

sink up to 40 mA and can be connected to a supply of up to 30V via an external current-limiting pull-up resistor (but the actual IC must use a 5V supply); *Figure 2.24* shows how one of these buffers can be used as a 5V to high-voltage (up to 30V) non-inverting interface. *Figure 2.25* shows how three o.c. buffers can be made to act as a wired-AND gate by wiring all three outputs to the same pull-up resistor; the circuit action is such that the output is pulled low when any input is low, and only goes high when all three inputs are high, thus giving an AND action.

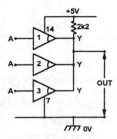

Figure 2.25  *Three 7407 buffers used to make a 3-input wired-AND gate.*

## Practical TTL inverter circuits

The inverter is the most basic of all TTL logic elements. Practical TTL inverters are often called inverting buffers, and usually have a fan-out of 10. If you need one or more inverters, you can either get them from a dedicated IC such as the 74LS04 Hex inverter (see *Figure 2.26*), or you can make them from spare NAND or NOR gates

Figure 2.26  *Functional diagram of the 74LS04 Hex inverter IC.*

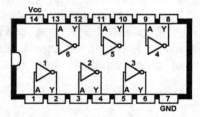

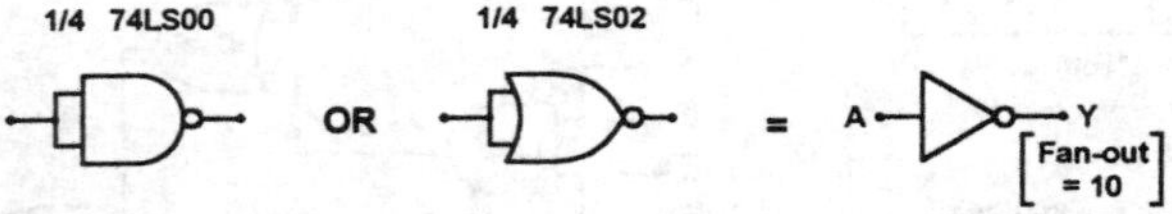

Figure 2.27  *Any NAND or NOR gate can be used as an inverting buffer element.*

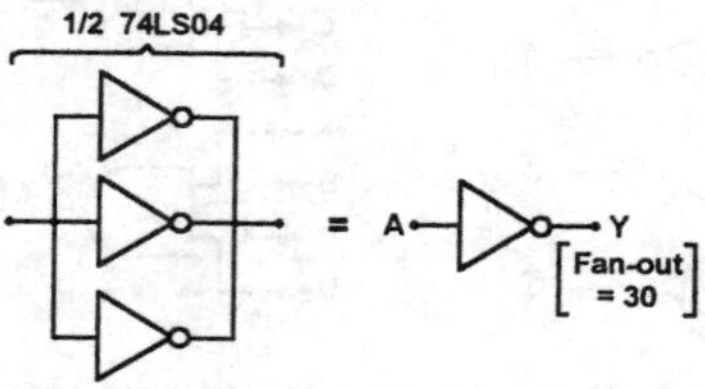

Figure 2.28  *Three 74LS04 inverters wired in parallel to give increased fan-out.*

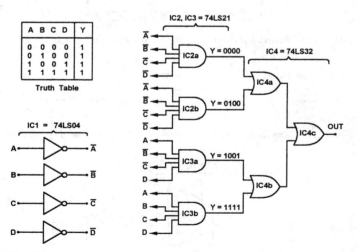

Figure 2.29  *All unused inverters must be connected in one of these ways.*

by connecting them as shown in *Figure 2.27*. If you need inverters with fan-outs greater than 10, you can either buy a high-fan-out IC, or you can boost the fan-outs of existing elements by parallel-connecting several inverters *from within the same IC package*, as shown in *Figure 2.28*. Note that all unused inverters must (to minimize their quiescent currents) be connected as shown in *Figure 2.29*, with their inputs wired to a logic-0 or ground point.

One particularly useful application of the inverter is as a complement generator in logic decoder systems, as shown in the circuit of *Figure 2.30* (which solves the same logic design problem as *Figure 2.9*). Here, each 4-bit (ABCD) input code is (by selecting a direct or inverted input) made available in an 'all logic-1' (= 1111) form via the four IC1 inverters, enabling any 4-bit code to be decoded via a 4-input AND gate (IC2 or IC3) as shown; IC4 is used as a 4-input OR gate, and its output goes to logic-1 when any one of the selected 4-bit input codes is present. Note that, by selecting

| A | B | C | D | Y |
|---|---|---|---|---|
| 0 | 0 | 0 | 0 | 1 |
| 0 | 1 | 0 | 0 | 1 |
| 1 | 0 | 0 | 1 | 1 |
| 1 | 1 | 1 | 1 | 1 |

Truth Table

Figure 2.30  *Four inverters used as a complement generator in a 4-bit 4-code decoder system.*

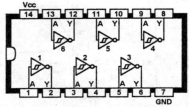

Figure 2.31   *Functional diagram of the 74LS14 Hex Schmitt inverter IC.*

appropriate direct or inverted inputs, this basic circuit can be used to decode any four combinations of 4-bit input codes.

The most useful inverter variant is the Schmitt type, and six of these are readily available in the 74LS14 IC (see *Figure 2.31*). In these Schmitt inverters the output is in the logic-1 state until the input *rises* to an 'upper threshold' value of 1.6V, at which point the output switches to logic-0 and locks there until the input is *reduced* to a 'lower threshold' value of 0.8V, at which point the output switches and locks into the logic-1 state again, and so on. Thus, a Schmitt inverter can be made to function as a sine-to-square generator by connecting it as shown in *Figure 2.32*, where RV1 is used to set the circuit to its maximum sensitivity point, at which a quiescent voltage of about 1.2V is set on the inverter's input.

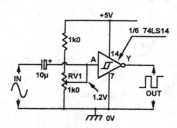

Figure 2.32   *Schmitt inverter sine-to-square converter.*

*Figures 2.33* to *2.35* show three more simple Schmitt inverter circuits. *Figure 2.33* is a practical version of the *Figure 1.47* switch debouncer; it can be activated by a push-button (S1) or toggle (S2) switch, and has an output that goes to logic-1 when the switch is closed. *Figure 2.34* is a modified version of the above circuit, with an added inverter stage, and gives a logic-0 output when S1 is closed. *Figure 2.35* is yet another modification of the basic circuit, and generates a brief logic-1 'switch-on' output pulse when the circuit's

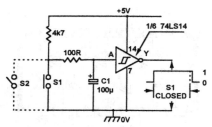

Figure 2.33  *Switch debouncer, with logic-1 'closed' output.*

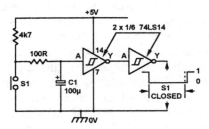

Figure 2.34  *Switch debouncer, with logic-0 'closed' output.*

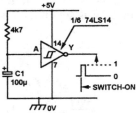

Figure 2.35  *Supply switch-on pulse generator.*

supply is first connected. Note that several more Schmitt inverter applications are shown in Chapter 3.

Schmitt inverters are also available in 3-state form, and *Figure 2.36* shows the functional diagram and Truth Table of the 74LS240 Octal 3-state Schmitt inverting buffer, in which each buffer has a fan-out of 30. This IC is actually a dual Quad device, in which inverters 1–4 are controlled via the CA terminal, and inverters 5–8 are controlled via the CB terminal. Each of these Quads can be used as a set of normal Schmitt inverters by grounding its control ter-

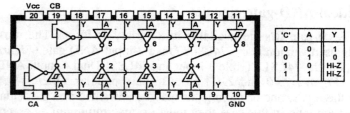

| 'C' | A | Y |
|-----|---|------|
| 0 | 0 | 1 |
| 0 | 1 | 0 |
| 1 | 0 | Hi-Z |
| 1 | 1 | Hi-Z |

Figure 2.36 *Functional diagram and Truth Table of the 74LS240 Octal (dual Quad) 3-state Schmitt inverting buffer IC.*

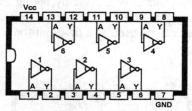

Figure 2.37 *Functional diagram of the 7406 Hex inverter with 30V o.c. outputs.*

minal, or as a ganged set of 3-state Schmitt inverters by using its control terminal as shown in the Truth Table.

TTL Hex inverter ICs are also available in versions with o.c. output stages, and the best known of these is the 7406 Standard-TTL device (see *Figure 2.37*), which – like the 7407 – can have its output connected to supplies of up to 30V via an external pull-up resistor (but the actual IC must use a 5V supply). The 7406 elements can be used as simple inverters with external pull-up resistors, or (by connecting them in a way similar to that shown in *Figure 2.24*) as '5V to high-voltage' inverting interfaces. They can also be used as wired-NOR gates by connecting them in the manner shown in the 3-input circuit of *Figure 2.38*, in which the output is pulled low if any input goes high.

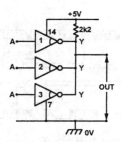

Figure 2.38 *Three 7406 inverters used to make a 3-input wired-NOR gate.*

## Practical AND-gate circuits

TTL AND-gate ICs are available in a variety of forms. The most widely used version is the 74LS08 Quad 2-input AND gate (*Figure 2.39*), but the 74LS11 Triple 3-input and 74LS21 Dual 4-input AND gates (*Figures 2.40* and *2.41*) are also very popular. Often, when using these ICs, one or more gates may be unwanted in a particular application, and in this case they must (to give minimum quiescent current consumption with good stability) be disabled by tying all of their inputs to logic-1; this is best done by taking the inputs to the positive supply rail via a single 1k0 resistor, as shown in *Figure 2.42*; a single resistor can be used as a tie-point for large numbers of unwanted inputs.

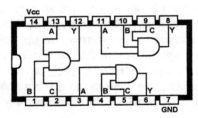

Figure 2.39 *74LS08 Quad 2-input AND gate IC.*

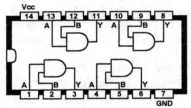

Figure 2.40 *74LS11 Triple 3-input AND gate IC.*

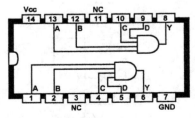

Figure 2.41 *74LS21 Dual 4-input AND gate IC.*

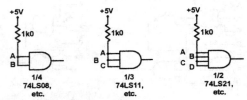

Figure 2.42 *Method of disabling unwanted AND gates.*

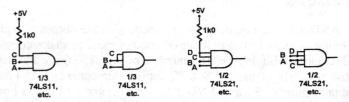

Figure 2.43 *Methods of disabling unwanted inputs, to make a 2-input AND gate.*

Figure 2.44 *Methods of using AND gates as simple buffers.*

Sometimes, when using 3-input or 4-input AND gate ICs, you will not want to use all of a gate's input terminals, and in this case the unwanted inputs can be disabled by either tying them high via a 1k0 resistor or by simply shorting them to a used input, in the manner shown in *Figure 2.43*. Note that the fan-in of an AND or NAND gate is an almost constant '1', irrespective of the number of inputs used. Thus, AND gates can be converted into non-inverting buffers by simply shorting all of there inputs together, as shown in *Figure 2.44*, and in each case will have a fan-in of 1.

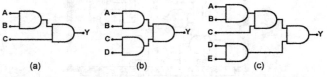

Figure 2.45 *Methods of using 74LS08 elements to make (a) 3-input, (b) 4-input, or (c) 5-input AND gates.*

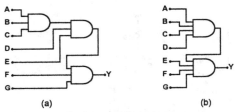

(a)                                (b)

Figure 2.46   *Methods of using (a) 74LS11 or (b) 74LS21 elements to make a 7-input AND gate.*

AND gates can be directly cascaded, with the output of one gate feeding directly into one input of another gate, to make compound AND gates with any desired number of inputs; *Figure 2.45* shows how elements of the 74LS08 IC can be interconnected to make 3-input, 4-input or 5-input AND gates, and *Figure 2.46* shows how the full capacity of a 74LS11 or 74LS21 IC can be used to make a 7-input AND gate.

## Practical NAND-gate circuits

The most widely used TTL NAND gate is the 74LS00 Quad 2-input type (see *Figure 2.47*), but the 74LS10 Triple 3-input, 74LS20 Dual 4-input and 74LS30 8-input NAND gates (see *Figures 2.48* to *2.50*) are also very popular. Some popular NAND gates have a Schmitt input action; the 74LS132 Quad 2-input Schmitt NAND gate has the same pin connections as the 74LS00, and the 74LS13 Dual 4-input Schmitt NAND gate has the same pin connections as the 74LS20.

Often, when using NAND-gate ICs, one or more gates may be unwanted in a particular application, and in this case they are best disabled by simply grounding their inputs as shown in *Figure 2.51*.

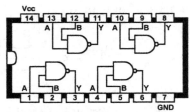

Figure 2.47   *74LS00 Quad 2-input NAND gate IC.*

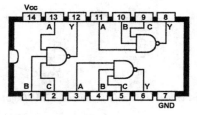

Figure 2.48   *74LS10 Triple 3-input NAND gate IC.*

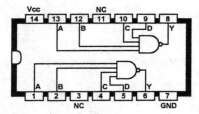

Figure 2.49   *74LS20 Dual 4-input NAND gate IC.*

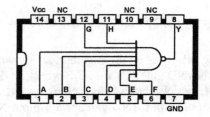

Figure 2.50   *74LS30 8-input NAND gate IC.*

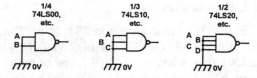

Figure 2.51   *Method of disabling unwanted NAND gates.*

Sometimes, when using NAND gates, you may not want to use all of the gate's input terminals, and in this case the unwanted inputs can be disabled by either tying them high via a 1k0 resistor or by simply shorting them to a used input, in the manner shown in *Figure 2.52*. Note that a NAND gate's fan-in is independent of the number of inputs used, and it can thus be made to act as an inverting buffer by

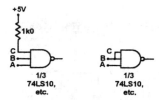

Figure 2.52   *Basic method of disabling unwanted NAND gate inputs.*

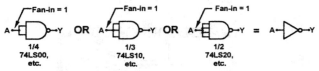

Figure 2.53   *Methods of using NAND gates as simple inverters.*

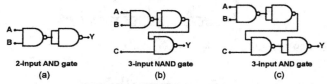

Figure 2.54   *Ways of using 74LS00 elements to make various AND and NAND gates.*

simply shorting all of its inputs together, as shown in *Figure 2.53*. Also note that NAND gate ICs are fairly versatile devices, as shown in *Figure 2.54*, which shows ways of using 74LS00 elements to make a 2-input or 3-input AND gate, or a 3-input NAND gate.

## Practical OR-gate circuits

Very few OR-gate ICs are available in TTL form. The most widely used device is the 74LS32 Quad 2-input OR-gate IC, which is shown in *Figure 2.55*. Often, when using this IC, one or more gates may be unwanted, and in this case they can be disabled by tying their inputs high, as shown in *Figure 2.56*. Note that the fan-in of an OR or NOR gate is directly proportional to the number of inputs used, at a fan-in rate of 1-per-input, and that a TTL 2-input OR gate can be made to act as a simple non-inverting buffer by either tying one input to ground or by tying both inputs together, as shown in *Figure 2.57*, but that the buffer has a fan-in of 1 in the former case, and a fan-in of 2 in the latter. Finally, note that OR gates can be directly cascaded to

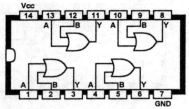

Figure 2.55  *74LS32 Quad 2-input OR gate IC.*

Figure 2.56  *Method of disabling an OR gate.*

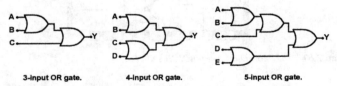

Figure 2.57  *Method of using an OR gate as a simple buffer.*

Figure 2.58  *Methods of cascading simple OR gates to give up to 5 inputs.*

make a compound OR gate with any desired number of inputs; *Figure 2.58*, for example, shows ways of cascading elements from a single 74LS32 to make OR gates with 3, 4 or 5 inputs.

## Practical NOR-gate circuits

The most widely used TTL NOR gate is the 74LS02 Quad 2-input type (see *Figure 2.59*), but the 74LS27 Triple 3-input and 74LS260 Dual 5-input NOR gates (see *Figures 2.60* and *2.61*) are also very popular. If, when using a NOR-gate IC, one or more of the gates are

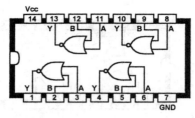

Figure 2.59 *74LS02 Quad 2-input NOR gate IC.*

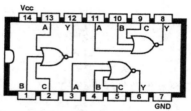

Figure 2.60 *74LS27 Triple 3-input NOR gate IC.*

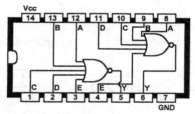

Figure 2.61 *74LS260 Dual 5-input NOR gate IC.*

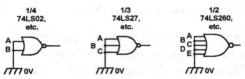

Figure 2.62 *Method of disabling a NOR gate.*

unwanted, they can be disabled by simply grounding their inputs as shown in *Figure 2.62*. Sometimes, when using NOR gates, you may not want to use all of the gate's input terminals, and in this case the unwanted inputs are best disabled by simply shorting them to ground, as shown in *Figure 2.63*. A NOR gate can be made to act as an inverting buffer by either shorting all of its inputs together or by

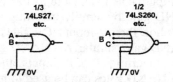

Figure 2.63 *Basic way of disabling unwanted NOR gate inputs.*

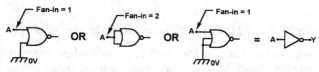

Figure 2.64 *Methods of using a NOR gate as a simple inverter.*

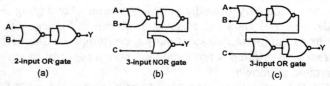

Figure 2.65 *Ways of using 74LS02 elements to make various OR and NOR gates.*

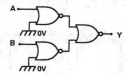

Figure 2.66 *NOR gates used to make a 2-input AND gate.*

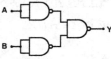

Figure 2.67 *NAND gates used to make a 2-input OR gate.*

grounding all but one of its inputs, as shown in *Figure 2.64*; note, however, that a NOR gate's fan-in is directly proportional to the number of inputs used, and the first method is thus (theoretically) the best, since it offers the lowest fan-in figure.

NOR-gate ICs are fairly versatile devices; *Figure 2.65* shows various ways of using 74LS02 elements to make 2-input or 3-input

OR gates, or a 3-input NOR gate. Note that a NOR gate can be converted into an AND gate by simply inverting all of its inputs, and *Figure 2.66* shows how three 2-input NOR gates can be used to make a single 2-input AND gate; similarly, a NAND gate can be converted into an OR gate by inverting all of its inputs, and *Figure 2.67* shows how three 2-input NAND gates can be used to make a single 2-input OR gate.

## Practical EX-OR- and EX-NOR-gate circuits

The output of an EX-OR gate goes high only when its two inputs are at different logic levels. The most widely used TTL EX-OR (EXclusive-OR) IC is the 74LS86 Quad EX-OR gate (see *Figure 2.68*). If one or more of an EX-OR IC's gates are unwanted, they can best be disabled by grounding one input terminal and tying the other to the +5V rail via a 1k0 resistor, as shown in *Figure 2.69*, as this results in minimum quiescent current consumption; alternatively, if current consumption is not important, both inputs can be simply tied to ground as shown.

EX-OR gates are reasonably versatile devices. An EX-OR gate can be made to act as a non-inverting buffer by shorting one input to ground, or as an inverting buffer by tying one input to the +5V rail

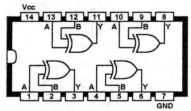

Figure 2.68   *74LS86 Quad EX-OR gate IC.*

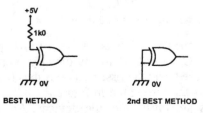

Figure 2.69   *Two ways of disabling unwanted EX-OR gates (see text).*

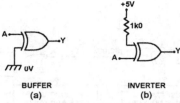

Figure 2.70 *Ways of using EX-OR gates as (a) buffers or (b) inverters.*

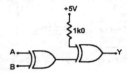

Figure 2.71 *An EX-NOR gate made from two EX-OR gates.*

via a 1k0 resistor, as shown in *Figure 2.70*. Thus, two EX-OR gates can be used to make a single EX-NOR gate by connecting them as shown in *Figure 2.71*, where the right-hand gate is used to invert the output of the left-hand gate (note that a Quad EX-NOR TTL IC is available in the form of the 74LS266, but this IC's gates have open-collector outputs).

EX-OR gates are exceptionally useful devices. *Figure 2.72*, for example, shows (in very basic form) how two EX-OR ICs can be used to make a digital data-scrambling system, in which scrambled DATA signals are sent along one communication link (a cable or wireless link, for example), and the de-scrambling code is sent along another link. Here, when the 'scrambling' signal is in the logic-0 state, both gates act as non-inverting buffers, and the DATA LINE and DATA OUTPUT signals are identical to the DATA INPUT signal; when the scrambling signal is in the logic-1 state both gates act as inverters, and the DATA INPUT and DATA OUTPUT signals are identical but the DATA LINE signals are inverted. Thus, when a

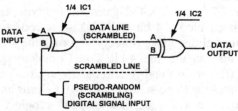

Figure 2.72 *Digital data scrambling system.*

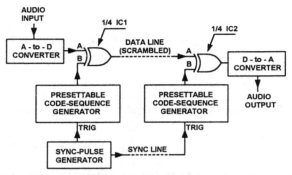

Figure 2.73   *Block diagram of a scrambled audio-communication system.*

random or pseudo-random digital 'scramble' signal is fed to input B of IC1, the DATA LINE signals are randomly scrambled, but are automatically unscrambled by IC2 if its B input is also fed with the same 'scramble' signal.

The basic *Figure 2.72* 'scrambling' system can be elaborated in many ways, and *Figure 2.73* shows – in block diagram form – how it can be turned into a high-security scrambled audio-communication system. Here, the audio input signal is fed to input A of IC1 via an analogue-to-digital (A-to-D) converter, and the input-B 'scramble' signal is derived from a pre-settable code-sequence generator, which is periodically triggered via a sync-pulse generator, which also triggers an identical code-sequence generator that feeds input B of IC2. IC2 thus provides an unscrambled digital output signal, and this is converted back into audio form via a D-to-A converter. Note that the system's presettable 'scramble' codes are self-contained at each end of the system and do not form part of the data link, and that the 'sync' signals can easily be mixed with the main DATA signals, enabling secure communication to be made over a single cable or wireless link.

*Figures 2.74* and *2.75* show two more useful EX-OR gate applications. In *Figure 2.74*, four EX-OR gates are fed with a common control signal that enabled a 4-bit 'ABCD' input code to be presented in the form of either a true (direct) or complement (inverted) ABCD output, thus making the 4-bit True/Complement outputs available via five (rather than eight) terminals. The circuit in *Figure 2.75* simply compares the logic-states of two 4-bit words and gives a logic-0 output if the two words are identical, and a logic-1 output if they differ.

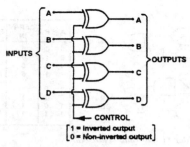

Figure 2.74 *4-bit True/Complement generator.*

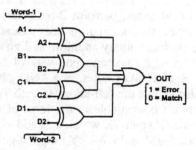

Figure 2.75 *4-bit logic-state comparator.*

One of the most important applications of the EX-OR gate is as a binary adder. *Figure 2.76* lists the basic rules of binary addition, and *Figure 2.77* shows how an EX-OR and an AND gate can be used to make a practical binary 'half-adder' circuit that can add two binary inputs together and generate SUM and CARRY outputs. The circuit is called a 'half-adder' because it can perform only a very primitive form of addition that does not enable it to accept a 'carry' input from

Figure 2.76 *Basic rules of binary addition.*

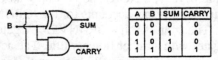

Figure 2.77 *Binary half-adder circuit.*

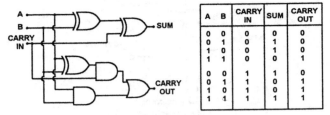

| A | B | CARRY IN | SUM | CARRY OUT |
|---|---|---|---|---|
| 0 | 0 | 0 | 0 | 0 |
| 0 | 1 | 0 | 1 | 0 |
| 1 | 0 | 0 | 1 | 0 |
| 1 | 1 | 0 | 0 | 1 |
| 0 | 0 | 1 | 1 | 0 |
| 0 | 1 | 1 | 0 | 1 |
| 1 | 0 | 1 | 0 | 1 |
| 1 | 1 | 1 | 1 | 1 |

Figure 2.78   *Full-adder circuit and Truth Table.*

a previous addition stage. A 'full-adder' is a far more useful circuit that can accept a 'carry' input, perform 2-bit binary addition, and generate a 'carry' output; such a circuit is fully cascadable, enabling groups of circuits to perform binary addition on digital numbers of a desired 'bit' size. *Figure 2.78* shows one way of building a full-adder circuit, using three EX-OR gates, two AND gates, and an OR gate; the diagram also shows the full-adder's Truth Table. Note that a 4-bit full-adder circuit is available in the form of the 74LS83 or 74LS283 TTL IC (see Chapter 7), which can add two 4-bit binary numbers and generate SUM and CARRY output signals.

## Mixed gate ICs

The '74' series of devices includes a number of 'mixed gate' ICs that contain gates of more than one type, wired together for use in specialized applications. The best known of these are known as 'AND–OR-INVERT' ('AOI') gates, and examples of these are shown in *Figures 2.79* and *2.80*. It is unlikely that you will ever need to use an AOI gate, but you may find it useful to learn some of the jargon that is associated with them. Looking first at the 7454 IC of *Figure 2.79*, note that it has input connections to four 2-input AND gates, and this accounts for the '4-wide 2-input AND–' part of the IC's title; also note that the outputs of these four AND gates are wired to the inputs of a NOR gate and thence made externally available via pin 8; now, a NOR gate is simply an OR gate with an inverted output, and this fact accounts for the 'OR-INVERT' part of the ICs title. Thus, an 'AND–OR-INVERT' gate is simply an 'AND–NOR gate' with a rather flowery title. The action of the 7454 IC is such that its output is normally high, and goes low only when both inputs to one or more AND gates are high.

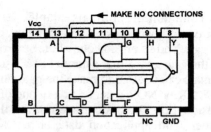

Figure 2.79 *7454 4-wide 2-input AND-OR-INVERT (AOI) gate IC.*

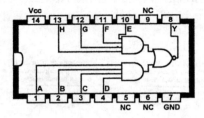

Figure 2.80 *74LS55 2-wide 4-input AND-OR-INVERT gate IC.*

Turning next to the 74LS55 IC of *Figure 2.80*, note that this has input connections to two 4-input AND gates, and this accounts for the IC's '2-wide 4-input AND–OR–INVERT' title; the IC's action is such that its output is normally high, and goes low only when all inputs to at least one AND gate are high.

Returning briefly to the 7454 IC, note that this is a Standard-TTL device, and its data sheet carries a very sinister warning that 'NO EXTERNAL CONNECTION' must be made to pins 11 and 12. Also note that the 'LS' version of this device (the 74LS54) has two of its four AND gates configured as 2-input types and two configured as 3-input types, and is sometimes known as a '4-wide, 2-3-3-2-input AND–OR–INVERT gate', and has pin connections, etc., that differ from those shown in *Figure 2.79*.

## Programmable logic ICs

Most logic ICs are dedicated devices that contain a number of 'fixed' gates. One very useful exception is a CMOS IC known as the 4048B 'programmable 8-input multifunction gate'. This low-cost 16-pin device has 8 input terminals, 2 output terminals, and 4 control terminals; one of the output terminals enables 4048B ICs to be cascaded, so that two of them make a 16-input gate, or four of them make a 32-input gate, and so on, and one of the control terminals can be used to make the gate give either a normal or a 3-state output. The other three terminals can be used to make the gate function as either an AND, NAND, OR or NOR gate, or as any one of four permutations of these basic types. The basic usage rules of this IC are fully described, together with application data on a CMOS 'majority logic' IC that can help resolve decision-making problems, in the author's *CMOS Circuits Manual* in the Newnes 'Circuits Manual' series.

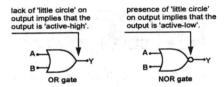

Figure 2.81   *Basic principle of 'assertion-level' logic notation.*

## Assertion-level logic notion

The reader is already familiar with the fact that an AND or OR gate has an 'active-high' output (i.e. the output of an OR gate goes high when any input is high, etc.), and with the MIL/ANSI convention that the addition of a little circle to an OR gate output (etc.) implies that the gate has an 'active low' output, as shown in *Figure 2.81*. Technically, the presence or absence of this 'little circle' is known as 'assertion-level logic notation', and it can be legitimately applied both to the input or the output of a logic symbol.

Thus, the crude 'gated pulse generator' symbol of *Figure 2.82a* implies that the pulse generator is gated on by a HIGH input signal, but the modified symbol of *Figure 2.82b* – in which a little circle is added to the generator's input – implies that this generator is gated

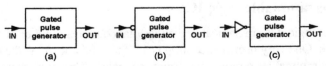

Figure 2.82   *Pulse generators that can be gated-on by (a) logic-1 and (b) and (c) logic-0 inputs.*

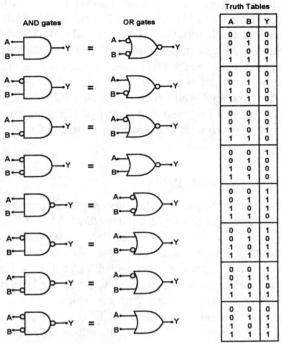

Figure 2.83 *Mixed logic equivalents.*

on by a LOW input signal, etc.; note that in practice the *Figure 2.82a* generator can be made to give the same action as that of *Figure 2.82b* by simply inserting an inverter stage between the IN terminal and the input of the generator, as shown in *Figure 2.82c*, so that a LOW input forces the generator's input HIGH and gates it on. This system of assertion-level logic notation is in fact very widely used in electronic logic symbology; some examples of its use are shown in *Figure 2.83*, which deals with mixed logic equivalents.

## Mixed logic equivalents

When assertion-level logic notation is applied to a simple 2-input AND or OR gate, it can be quickly seen that the gate has four possible input assertion-level sets, i.e. both inputs active-HIGH, or both active-LOW, or one active-HIGH and one active-LOW, or vice versa. Similarly, the gate's output has two possible assertion-levels (active-HIGH or active-LOW). Thus, a 2-input AND or OR gate has a total of eight possible input/output assertion-levels. If Truth Tables are drawn up for all sixteen possible AND and OR gate variations, it becomes apparent that each AND gate variation has a mixed-logic OR gate equivalent, and vice versa, as shown in *Figure 2.83*. Note in particular that a normal AND gate can be simulated by a NOR gate with both inputs inverted, and that a normal OR gate can be simulated by a NAND gate with both inputs inverted, etc.

## Digital 'transmission' gates

Most logic-gate circuits presented in this chapter show the gates used as simple logic-state detectors. 2-input AND, NAND, OR and NOR gates can, however, also be used as digital 'transmission' gates which pass a digital input signal only when they are 'opened' by an appropriate control signal or logic-level. Transmission gates are available in four basic types, and the logic symbols of these are shown, together with their logic-gate equivalents, in *Figure 2.84*. The basic transmission gate (*Figure 2.84a*) gives a non-inverted output and can be opened by a logic-1 control signal, and can be simulated by a 2-input AND gate; this transmission gate can be made to give an inverted output, as in (*Figure 2.84b*), by using a NAND gate instead of an AND gate. Another variation of the basic transmission gate is shown in *Figure 2.84c*; it gives a non-inverted output

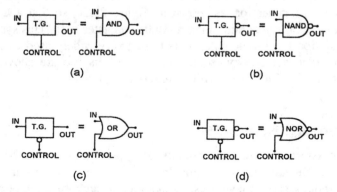

Figure 2.84  *Four basic types of digital transmission gate, with their 2-input logic-gate equivalents.*

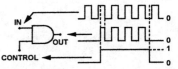

Figure 2.85   *AND-type transmission gate is opened by logic-1 control and gives normally-low non-inverted output.*

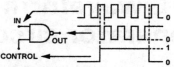

Figure 2.86   *NAND-type transmission gate is opened by logic-1 control and gives normally-high inverted output.*

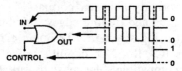

Figure 2.87   *OR-type transmission gate is opened by logic-0 control and gives normally-high non-inverted output.*

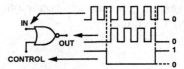

Figure 2.88   *NOR-type transmission gate is opened by logic-0 control and gives normally-low inverted output.*

but is opened by a logic-0 control signal, and can be simulated by a 2-input OR gate; this gate can be made to give an inverted output, as in *Figure 2.84d*, by using a NOR gate instead of an OR gate. Finally, to conclude this Chapter, *Figures 2.85* to *2.88* show the precise relationships between the input, output and control signals of each of these four types of transmission gate.

# 3 TTL waveform generator circuits

TTL ICs must, in general, be driven or clocked by clean input waveforms that switch abruptly between normal TTL logic-levels and have very sharp leading and trailing edges; suitable waveforms can be easily generated using standard TTL logic elements or special waveform-generator ICs. If a TTL circuit's initial input waveforms are not fully TTL compatible they must be suitably modified via special waveform-conditioning circuitry before being passed on to the inputs of the main TTL IC networks. This chapter looks at a wide range of digital waveform generator and conditioner circuits suitable for use with modern TTL circuitry.

## Waveform generator basics

Most digital waveform generator circuits fit into one or other of the four basic categories shown in *Figure 3.1*. Schmitt trigger circuits (*Figure 3.1a*) produce an output that switches abruptly between logic-0 and logic-1 values whenever an input signal goes above or below preset instantaneous voltage levels. Circuits of this type can thus be used in waveform-shaper applications, such as converting a sine or ramp input waveform into a square- or pulse-shaped output, for example.

Simple bistable circuits (*Figure 3.1b*) have two input terminals, known as SET and RESET. The circuit's output can be latched into the logic-1 state by applying a suitable command signal (usually a brief logic-1 pulse) to the SET input terminal; the output can then be latched into the alternative logic-0 state only by applying a suitable command signal to the RESET terminal, and so on. 'Latch' circuits

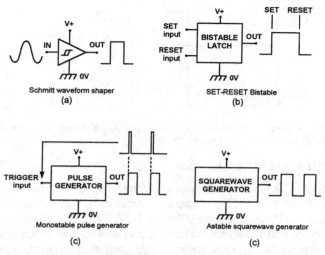

Figure 3.1 *Four basic types of digital waveform generator circuit.*

of this type are useful in a variety of digital signal-conditioning applications.

Monostable circuits (*Figure 3.1c*) have an output that switches high on the arrival of an input trigger signal, but then automatically switches back to the low state again after some preset time delay. Circuits of this basic type thus act as triggered pulse generators.

Astable circuits (*Figure 3.1d*) have an output that switches into the logic-1 state for a preset period, then switches into the logic-0 state for a second preset period, and then switches back into the first state again, and so on. Circuits of this basic type thus generate a free-running squarewave output.

In practice, all of these basic circuits can be elaborated into more complex forms. The simple bistable circuit, for example, can be elaborated into the form of the triggered flip-flop, which changes its output state each time a new trigger pulse reaches it via a single input terminal. The simple monostable can be elaborated into a 'resettable' form, in which the output pulse can be terminated prematurely via a 'reset' signal, or into a 'retriggerable' form, in which a new monostable timing period is initiated each time a new trigger pulse arrives. Astable circuits may be completely free-running, or may be 'gated' types which operate only in the presence of a suitable gate signal, etc. Practical circuits of all these types are described in this chapter.

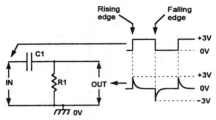

Figure 3.2 *A simple C-R coupler can be used to distinguish between the 'rising' and 'falling' edges of a digital waveform.*

## Schmitt waveform shapers

A number of Schmitt sine/square converter, switch 'debouncer', and supply switch-on pulse generator circuits have already been described in Chapter 2 (see *Figures 2.32* to *2.35*). These are all, basically, Schmitt waveform shapers, and another useful application of this type of circuit is as an 'edge'-detector that produces a useful output pulse on the arrival of either the leading or the trailing edge of a digital input waveform. The basic principle of 'edge'-detection can be understood with the help of *Figure 3.2*. Here, a 3V squarewave input signal is applied to the input of a simple C–R coupler that has a time-constant that is very short relative to the period of the input waveform; the coupler's action is such that its output switches abruptly to +3V on the arrival of the squarewave's

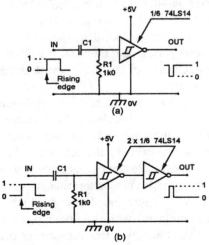

Figure 3.3 *Rising-edge detector giving (a) negative-going or (b) positive-going output pulse.*

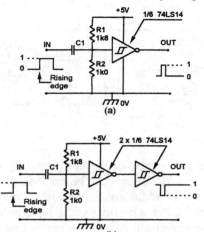

Figure 3.4  *Falling-edge detector giving (a) positive-going or (b) negative-going output pulse.*

'rising' edge but then decays rapidly to zero-volts as C1 charges up via R1, and switches abruptly to −3V on the arrival of the square wave's 'falling' edge but then decays rapidly to zero-volts as C1 discharges via R1, and so on.

Thus, the C–R coupler generates a positive spike on the arrival of a rising input edge, and a negative spike on the arrival of a falling edge. *Figure 3.3a* shows how this coupler can be used in conjunction with a TTL Schmitt inverter to make a pulse-generating rising-edge detector. Here, R1 normally ties the Schmitt input low, so that its output is at logic-1, but on the arrival of the input rising edge the R1 positive spike drives the Schmitt output briefly to logic-0, so that it generates a negative-going output pulse. Note that, since the Schmitt's input is normally tied low, the negative 'falling edge' input spikes have no effect on the circuit. *Figure 3.3b* shows how the circuit can be made to give a positive-going output pulse by simply taking the output via another Schmitt inverter.

*Figure 3.4a* shows how the basic circuit can be modified so that it generates a positive-going output pulse on the arrival of a falling (rather than rising) input edge. Here, the Schmitt's input is normally biased above its 1.6V upper threshold value via the R1–R2 divider, so it ignores the effects of positive 'rising edge' spikes, and its output is normally at logic-0. But on the arrival of each negative 'falling edge' spike its input is driven below the Schmitt's 0.8V lower

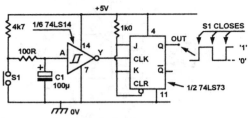

Figure 3.5 *Push-to-toggle 'switching' circuit.*

threshold value, and it generates a positive-going output pulse. *Figure 3.4b* shows how the circuit can be made to give a negative-going output pulse via an additional Schmitt inverter stage.

Note from *Figure 3.2* that a positive-going input pulse has a rising leading edge and a falling trailing edge, so in this case a rising-edge detector acts as a 'leading-edge' detector. But a negative-going input pulse has a falling leading edge and a rising trailing edge, so in this case a rising-edge detector acts as a 'trailing-edge' detector. Also note that the output pulse widths of circuits in *Figure 3.3* and *3.4* vary greatly with individual ICs, but roughly equal 1μs per nF of C1 value.

*Figure 3.5* shows another useful application of the Schmitt waveform shaper. In this case the Schmitt is wired as a switch debouncer (see *Figure 2.33*) but has its output fed to the CLOCK terminal of a clocked JK flip-flop (see Chapter 4), which changes its output state each time a new clock pulse arrives. Thus, the output changes its logic level each time S1 is closed, and S1 is thus given an effective 'toggling' action.

## Bistable waveform generators

A bistable waveform generator is a circuit that can have its output set to either the logic-1 or logic-0 state by applying a suitable control signal to either its SET or RESET input terminal. The simplest way to make a circuit of this type is to wire a pair of normal or Schmitt inverter elements into a feedback loop as shown in *Figure 3.6*. If RESET switch S1 is briefly closed it shorts the A input low, driving the A output and B input high, thus making the B output go low and lock the A input into the low state irrespective of the subsequent state of S1. The circuit thus latches into this RESET state, with its output

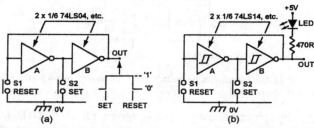

Figure 3.6 *These manually-triggered bistable circuits can be built from either (a) normal or (b) Schmitt inverter elements.*

at logic-0, until SET switch S2 is briefly closed, at which point the B output and A input are driven high, thus making the A output go low and lock the B input into the low state irrespective of the subsequent state of S2. The circuit thus latches into this SET state, with its output at logic-1, until the S1 RESET switch is next closed, at which point the whole sequence starts to repeats.

Note that each time S1 (or S2) is operated, it places a short between the B (or A) output and ground, but that the resultant output current is internally limited to safe values by the inverter's totem-pole output stage and only effectively flows for the few nanoseconds that are taken (by the circuit) to switch the inverter into its latched 'output low' state. These apparently-brutal circuits are thus, in reality, soundly engineered and are delightfully cheap and effective designs that generate perfectly 'bounce-free' output switching wave-forms. If desired, the circuit's output state can be monitored by a LED connected as shown in *Figure 3.6b*, so that the LED glows when the output is in the 'RESET' (low) state. The basic design can be modified for operation via a single toggle switch by connecting it as shown in the circuit of *Figure 3.7*, which generates a perfectly reliable and bounce-free 'toggle' output waveform.

The basic *Figure 3.6* and *3.7* circuits are not really suitable for

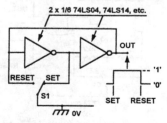

Figure 3.7 *This 'bistable toggle switch' gives perfect waveform generation from a normal toggle switch.*

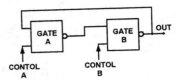

Figure 3.8   *A bistable latch can be built by interconnecting two NAND or NOR 2-input gates as shown.*

activation by electronic trigger-pulse signals, etc., but can be adapted for this operation by replacing the simple inverters with 2-input NAND or NOR gates connected as shown in *Figure 3.8*, so that the control inputs are not subjected to odd loading effects. If NAND gates are used, both inputs must normally be biased high, and the output is SET by briefly pulling control B low, etc. If NOR gates are used, both inputs must normally be biased low, and the output is SET by briefly driving control A high, etc.

*Figure 3.9* shows ways of using a NAND-type SET–RESET (S–R) bistable as a manually-triggered 'toggle' waveform generator that is activated via either two push-button switches (*Figure 3.9a*) or a single toggle switch (*Figure 3.9b*). These diagrams act as handy

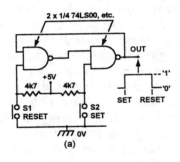

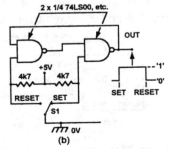

Figure 3.9   *NAND bistables used as manually-triggered 'toggle' waveform generators.*

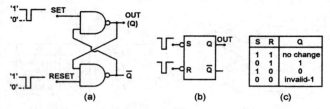

Figure 3.10 *Conventional schematic (a), symbol (b), and Truth Table of the NAND-type S–R bistable or flip-flop.*

'wiring' guides, but note that the conventional way of drawing the NAND bistable is in *Figure 3.10a*. The NAND bistable is a standard logic element, and is usually called an S–R (or R–S) bistable or flip-flop; *Figure 3.10b* shows its international circuit symbol, in which the little negation circle on each input indicates that it is activated by logic-0 levels, and which has both normal (Q) and inverted (NOT-Q) outputs; *Figure 3.10c* shows the element's Truth Table, which indicates that both inputs must normally be biased high (to logic-1), and that the element goes into an 'invalid' state – with both outputs set to logic-1 – if both inputs are low at the same time.

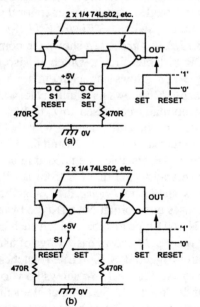

Figure 3.11 *NOR bistables used as manually-triggered 'toggle' waveform generators.*

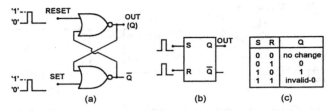

Figure 3.12 *Conventional schematic (a), symbol (b), and Truth Table (c) of the NOR-type S–R (or R–S) bistable or flip-flop.*

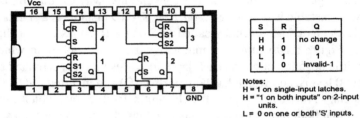

Figure 3.13 *Functional diagram of the 74LS279 Quad S–R latch IC.*

*Figure 3.11* shows ways of using a NOR-type S–R bistable as a manually-triggered 'toggle' waveform generator that is activated via either two push-button switches (*Figure 3.11a*) or a single toggle switch (*Figure 3.11b*). *Figure 3.12a* shows the conventional way of drawing the NOR bistable circuit, which is also a standard logic element; *Figure 3.12b* shows the element's international circuit symbol, and *Figure 3.12c* shows its Truth Table, which indicates that both inputs must normally be biased low (to logic-0), and that the element goes into an 'invalid' state – with both outputs set to logic 0 – if both inputs are high at the same time.

If more than two S–R bistables are needed in any application, the most cost-effective way to get them is from a 74LS279 Quad S-R latch IC, which is shown in *Figure 3.13*, together with its Truth Table. This IC houses two normal NAND-type bistables (elements 2 and 4), plus two NAND-type bistables which each have two SET (S1 and S2) inputs. *Figure 3.14* shows basic ways of using 74LS279 elements as manually-triggered SET–RESET latches; *Figures 3.14b* and *c* show how to use *Figure 3.14a* shows how to use a simple '2' or '4' element in this mode; '2-SET'-input elements by either tying both SET terminals together, or by tying one input to logic-1 and applying the SET signal to the other.

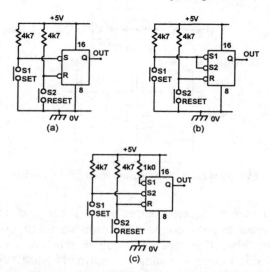

Figure 3.14 *Basic ways of using 74LS279 elements as SET-RESET latches.*

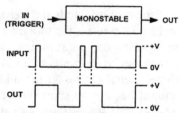

Figure 3.15 *A standard monostable generates an accurate output pulse on the arrival of a suitable trigger signal.*

## Monostable pulse generators

A monostable ('mono') or 'one-shot' pulse generator is a circuit that generates a single high-quality output pulse of some specific width or period $p$ on the arrival of a suitable trigger signal. In a standard monostable circuit the arrival of the trigger signal initiates an internal timing cycle which causes the monostable output to change state at the start of the timing cycle, but to revert back to its original state on completion of the cycle, as shown in *Figure 3.15*. Note that once a timing cycle has been initiated the standard monostable circuit is immune to the effects of subsequent trigger signals until its timing period ends naturally, but it then needs a certain 'recovery' time (usually equal to $p$ or greater) to fully reset before it can again gen-

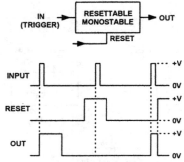

Figure 3.16    *The output pulse of a resettable mono can be aborted by a suitable reset pulse.*

erate an *accurate* triggered output pulse; it can thus not normally generate accurate pulse output waveforms with duty cycles greater than about 50%. This type of circuit is sometimes modified by adding a RESET control terminal, as shown in *Figure 3.16*, to enable the output pulse to be terminated or aborted at any time via a suitable command signal.

Another variation of the monostable is the 'retriggerable' circuit. Here, the trigger signal actually resets the mono and almost simultaneously initiates a new pulse-generating timing cycle, as shown in *Figure 3.17*, so that each new trigger signal initiates a new timing cycle, even if the trigger signal arrives in the midst of an existing cycle. This type of circuit has a very short recovery time, and can generate accurate pulse output waveforms with duty cycles up to almost 100%.

Most monostables are 'edge' triggered, i.e., their pulse generation cycle is initiated (fired) by the arrival of the trigger signal's rising or falling edge; this type of mono needs a well shaped trigger signal, with fast edges. Some monostables, however, are 'voltage level' trig-

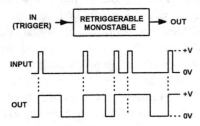

Figure 3.17    *A retriggerable mono starts a new timing cycle on the arrival of each new trigger signal.*

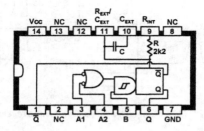

Figure 3.18   *Functional diagram, etc., of the 74121 'standard' triggered monostable IC.*

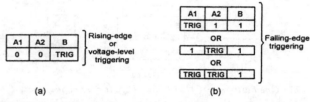

Figure 3.19   *Basic 74121 connections for (a) rising-edge or (b) falling-edge triggering.*

gered via a Schmitt input stage, and fire when the voltage reaches a predetermined value; this type of mono can be fired by any shape of input signal.

Thus, the circuit designer may use an edge triggered or level triggered standard mono, resettable mono, or retriggerable mono to generate triggered output pulses. In TTL circuitry, the most cost-effective way of generating these high quality output pulses is via a dedicated TTL pulse-generator IC, and three low-cost devices of this type (the 74121, 74LS123 and 74LS221) are readily available.

*Figure 3.18* shows the functional diagram, etc., of the 74121. This old but very popular 'standard' monostable pulse generator IC can give useful output pulse widths from 30ns to hundreds of ms via (usually) two external timing components, and can be configured to give either level-sensitive rising-edge or simple falling-edge triggering action. Note that the IC has three available trigger-input terminals; of these, A1 and A2 are used as falling-edge triggering inputs, and B functions as a level-sensitive Schmitt rising-edge triggering input; *Figure 3.19* shows how to connect these inputs for specific types of trigger action.

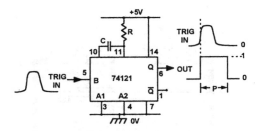

Figure 3.20    *Basic 74121 rising-edge or voltage-level triggering connections.*

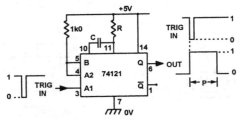

Figure 3.21    *One basic set of 74121 falling-edge trigger connections.*

Thus, for rising-edge or voltage level triggering, A1 and A2 must be grounded and the trigger input is applied to B, as shown in *Figure 3.20* (which also shows the two external timing components wired in place). For falling-edge triggering, B must be tied to logic-1, and the trigger input must be applied to A1 and/or A2, but the unused 'A' input (if any) must be tied to logic-1; *Figure 3.21* shows an example of one of these options, with B and A2 tied to logic-1, and the trigger input applied to A1.

Dealing next with this IC's timing circuitry, note that the 74121 has three timing-component terminals. A low-value timing capacitor is built into the IC and can be augmented by external capacitors wired between pins 10 and 11 (on polarized capacitors the '+' terminal must go to pin 11). The IC also incorporates a 2k0 timing resistor that is used by connecting pin 9 to pin 14 either directly or via a resistance of up to 40k; alternatively, the internal resistor can be ignored and an external resistance (1k4 to 40k) can be wired between pin 11 and pin 14. Whichever connection is used, the output pulse width = $0.7R_TC_T$, where width is in milliseconds, $R_T$ is the *total* timing resistance, and $C_T$ is the timing capacitance in microfarads. Note that the circuits of *Figures 3.20* and *3.21* show the normal methods of using the 74121, with external timing resistors and capacitors.

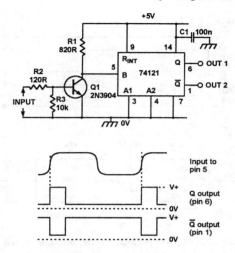

**Figure 3.22** *30ns pulse generator using 'B' input (Schmitt) rising-edge or voltage-level triggering.*

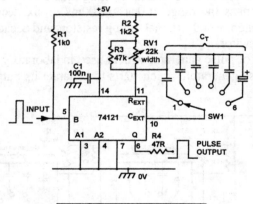

| SW1 RANGE | $C_T$ VALUE | PULSE-WIDTH RANGE |
|---|---|---|
| 1 | 100pF | 100nS - 1μS |
| 2 | 1n0 | 1μS - 10μS |
| 3 | 10n | 0μS - 100μS |
| 4 | 100n | 100μS - 1mS |
| 5 | 1μ0 | 1mS - 10mS |
| 6 | 10μ | 10mS - 100mS |

**Figure 3.23** *This high-performance add-on pulse generator spans 100ns to 100ms.*

*Figure 3.22* shows the 74121 used as a 30ns pulse generator, using only the IC's internal timing components, and with its trigger signal connected to the B (Schmitt) input via a simple transistor

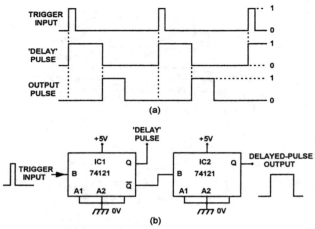

Figure 3.24  *Basic delayed-pulse generator waveforms and circuit.*

buffer stage, and *Figure 3.23* shows it used to make an add-on pulse generator that can be used with an existing squarewave 'trigger' generator and spans the range 100ns to 100ms in six decade ranges, using both internal and external timing resistors and decade-switched external capacitors.

One type of pulse generator widely used in laboratory work is the delayed-pulse generator, which starts to generate its output pulse at

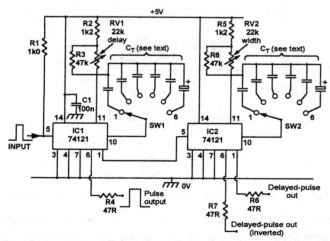

Figure 3.25  *High-performance add-on delayed-pulse generator spans 100ns to 100ms.*

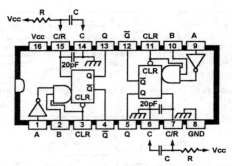

Figure 3.26 *Functional diagram and basic external timing-component connections of the 74LS123 Dual retriggerable monostable with CLEAR.*

some specified delay-time *after* the application of the initial trigger signal. *Figure 3.24a* shows the typical waveforms of this type of generator, and *Figure 3.24b* shows the basic way of making such a generator from two 74121 ICs. Here, the trigger input signal fires IC1, which generates a 'delay' pulse, and as this pulse ends its inverted (NOT-Q) output fires IC2, which generates the final (delayed) output pulse.

*Figure 3.25* shows how two of the basic *Figure 3.23* circuits can be coupled together to make a practical 'add-on' wide-range delayed-pulse generator in which both the 'delay' and 'output pulse' periods are fully variable from 100ns to 100ms. Note in this circuit that both fixed-amplitude inverted and non-inverted outputs are short-circuit protected via 47R series resistors. This circuit's timing periods and $C_T$ values are identical to those listed in the table of *Figure 3.23*.

*Figure 3.26* shows the functional diagram of the 74LS123 Dual retriggerable monostable with CLEAR, together with basic connections for its external timing components (R and C); note that pins 6 and 14 are internally connected to pin 8 (ground), and that internal capacitances of about 20pF exist between pins 6–7 and pins 14–15. In this IC, each mono has three input trigger-control terminals, notated A, B and CLR. Normally, CLR must be biased to logic-1 (via a 1k0 resistor); it sets the Q output at logic-0 when CLR is pulled low.

The 74LS123 can be triggered in three different modes via the A, B, and CLR terminals, as shown in *Figures 3.27* and *3.28*. It can be triggered in the rising-edge mode by tying A to logic-0, CLR to logic-1, and applying the trigger signal to B, as shown in *Figure*

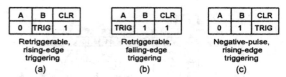

| A | B | CLR |
|---|---|---|
| 0 | TRIG | 1 |

Retriggerable,
rising-edge
triggering
(a)

| A | B | CLR |
|---|---|---|
| TRIG | 1 | 1 |

Retriggerable,
falling-edge
triggering
(b)

| A | B | CLR |
|---|---|---|
| 0 | 1 | TRIG |

Negative-pulse,
rising-edge
triggering
(c)

Figure 3.27   *Basic 74LS123 connections for three different triggering modes.*

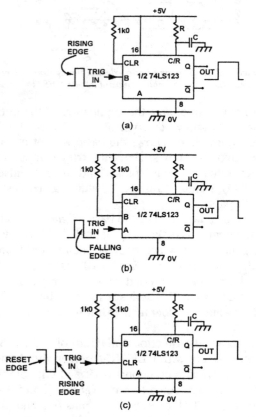

Figure 3.28   *Basic ways of using a 74LS123 to give (a) rising-edge, (b) falling-edge, or (c) Negative-pulse rising-edge triggering.*

3.28a, or in the falling-edge mode by tying B and CLR to logic-1 and applying the trigger signal to A, as shown in *Figure 3.28b*. The third 'negative-pulse rising-edge' mode – shown in *Figure 3.28c* – is rarely used; here, A is set to logic-0, B and CLR are biased to logic-1, and the negative-going trigger pulse is applied to CLR; the falling-

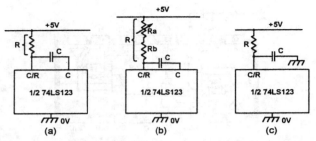

Figure 3.29 *Alternative ways of connecting 74LS123 timing components.*

edge of this pulse resets the monostable, and the rising-edge triggers a new monostable period.

Dealing next with the 74LS123's timing network, this consists of an external resistance (5k0 to 260k) connected between the C/R terminal and the positive supply line, and a capacitance (of any appropriate value) connected between C/R and either the 'C' terminal or ground; *Figure 3.29* shows three alternative ways of connecting these components. The 74LS123's timing period is given approximately by:

$$p = 0.4R_{T}C_{T},$$

where $p$ = pulse width in nanoseconds, $R_{T}$ = resistance in kilohms, and $C_{T}$ = *total* capacitance (including the internal 20pF) in pF; thus, external values of 25k and 10nF give pulse widths of about 100μs, for example. Note that these values are subject to some variation between individual ICs, and with variations in supply voltage and temperature (typically up to ±1% over the IC's voltage range, and up to ±2% over its operating temperature range).

Before leaving the 74LS123, note that if you have an application where you only need to use one of this excellent IC's monostables, the unwanted monostable should be disabled by tying its CLR terminal high and grounding its A and B terminals, as shown in *Figure 3.30*.

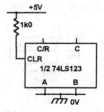

Figure 3.30 *Method of disabling an unwanted 74LS123 monostable.*

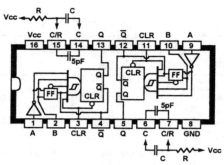

Figure 3.31 *Functional diagram and basic external timing-component connections of the 74LS221 Dual precision Schmitt-triggered monostable with CLEAR.*

Finally, *Figure 3.31* shows the functional diagram of the 74LS221 Dual precision Schmitt-triggered monostable with CLEAR, together with basic connections for its external timing components (R and C); note that the external C must be connected between pins 6–7 or 14–15, and that these pins are shunted by an internal capacitance of about 5pF. Also note that the 74LS221 is NOT a retriggerable IC, and is thus subject to the normal duty-cycle limitations of an ordinary monostable; the IC should in fact be regarded as an improved high-performance Dual version of the old 74121 (at the time of writing, it costs less than half the 74121 price). In the 74LS221, each mono has three Schmitt-type input trigger-control terminals, notated A, B and CLR, with semi-latching action on B and CLR via an internal NAND-type flip-flop (FF). Normally, CLR must be biased to logic-1 (via a 1k0 resistor); it sets the Q output at logic-0 if it is pulled low.

The 74LS221 can be triggered in three different modes via the A, B and CLR terminals, as shown in *Figures 3.32* and *3.33*. It can be triggered in the rising-edge mode by tying A to logic-0, CLR to logic-1, and applying the trigger signal to B, as shown in *Figure 3.33a*, or in the falling-edge mode by tying B and CLR to logic-1 and applying the trigger signal to A, as shown in *Figure 3.33b*. The third

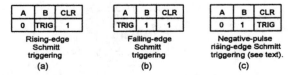

| A | B | CLR |
|---|---|---|
| 0 | TRIG | 1 |

Rising-edge
Schmitt
triggering
(a)

| A | B | CLR |
|---|---|---|
| TRIG | 1 | 1 |

Falling-edge
Schmitt
triggering
(b)

| A | B | CLR |
|---|---|---|
| 0 | 1 | TRIG |

Negative-pulse
rising-edge Schmitt
triggering (see text).
(c)

Figure 3.32 *Basic 74LS221 connections for three different triggering modes.*

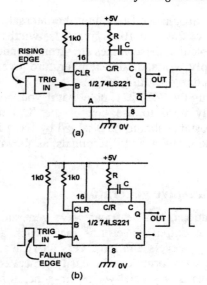

Figure 3.33 *Basic ways of using a 74LS221 to give (a) rising-edge or (b) falling-edge Schmitt triggering action.*

'negative-pulse rising-edge' mode is rarely used; here, A is set to logic-0, and the circuit is then primed by switching B from logic-0 to logic-1 while CLR is held at logic-0; then, with B at logic-1, a rising-edge on CLR will trigger a monostable period.

Dealing next with the 74LS221's timing network, this consists of an external resistance (1k4 to 100k) connected between the C/R terminal and the positive supply line, and a capacitance (of any value up to 1000μF) connected between C/R and the C terminal, as shown in *Figure 3.33*. The 74LS221's timing period is given approximately by:

$$p = 0.7R_TC_T,$$

where $p$ = pulse width in nanoseconds, $R_T$ = resistance in kilohms,

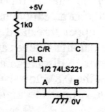

Figure 3.34 *Method of disabling an unwanted 74LS221 monostable.*

and $C_T$ = *total* capacitance (including the internal 5pF) in pF; thus, external values of 25k and 10nF give pulse widths of about 175µs, for example. Note that these values are virtually independent of variations in supply voltage and temperature over the IC's full voltage/temperature operating range.

Before leaving the 74LS221, note that if you have an application where you only need to use one of the IC's monostables, the unwanted monostable should be disabled by tying its CLR terminal high and grounding its A and B terminals, as shown in *Figure 3.34*.

## Astable squarewave generators

In TTL applications, astable squarewave generators must produce clean and stable output waveforms that switch abruptly between normal TTL logic-levels and have very sharp leading and trailing edges; suitable waveforms can be easily generated using standard TTL logic elements or special waveform-generator ICs. The easiest and most cost-effective way to make a TTL astable is to use a 74LS14 or similar Schmitt inverter element in the basic circuit of *Figure 3.35*, which operates as follows.

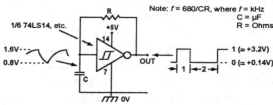

Figure 3.35   *Basic circuit and waveforms, etc., of a Schmitt astable.*

Suppose in *Figure 3.35* that C's voltage has just fallen to the Schmitt's lower threshold value of 0.8V, making the Schmitt's output switch to logic-1; under this condition the Schmitt output is at about +3.2V, so C starts to charge exponentially upwards from 0.8V until it reaches the 1.6V upper threshold value of the Schmitt, at which point the Schmitt's output switches abruptly to a logic-0 value of about 0.14V, and C starts to discharge exponentially downwards from 1.6V until it reaches the 0.8V lower threshold value, at which point the Schmitt's output switches to logic-1 again, and the whole process repeats, and so on.

This simple Schmitt astable circuit generates a useful but non-symmetrical squarewave output; its Mark–Space ratio is about 1:2 (i.e. it has a 33% duty cycle), and its operating frequency ($f$) approximately equals $680/(CR)$, where $C$ is in µF, $R$ (which can have any value in the 100R to 1k2 range) is in ohms, and $f$ is in kHz; thus, $C$ and $R$ values of 100nF and 1k0 give an operating frequency about 6.8kHz, for example. Note that the operating frequency has a slight positive temperature coefficient, and has a supply voltage coefficient of about +0.5%/100mV. The circuit can, in theory, operate at frequencies ranging from below 1Hz ($C = 1000$µF) to above 10MHz ($c = 50$pF), but in practice is best limited to the approximate frequency range 400Hz–2MHz, because the need for large $c$ values makes it uneconomic at low frequencies, and it has poor stability at high frequencies.

The basic Schmitt astable circuit can be usefully modified in a variety of ways. The operating frequency can, for example, be made variable by using a fixed 100R and variable 1k0 resistor in the R position, and the output waveform can be improved by feeding it through a Schmitt buffer stage, as shown in *Figure 3.36*. If perfect waveform symmetry is needed, it can be obtained by feeding the output of a buffered Schmitt astable through a JK flip-flop, as shown in *Figure 3.37*, but note that the final output frequency is half of that of the astable. The basic circuit can be converted into a gated Schmitt

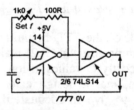

Figure 3.36 *Variable-frequency buffered-output Schmitt astable.*

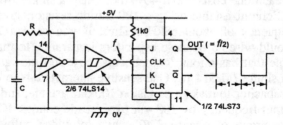

Figure 3.37 *Schmitt astable with precise 1:1 Mark–Space ratio output.*

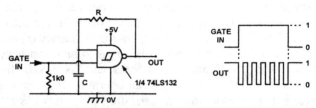

Figure 3.38 *Gated Schmitt astable with logic-1 gate-on and normally-high output.*

astable by using a 74LS132 2-input Schmitt NAND gate as its basic element, as shown in *Figure 3.38*; this particular circuit is gated on by a logic-1 input and has a normally-high (logic-1) output; it can be made to give a normally-low (logic-0) output by feeding the output through a spare 74LS132 element connected as a simple Schmitt inverter, as shown in *Figure 3.39*.

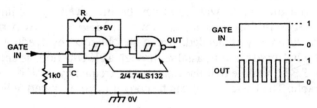

Figure 3.39 *Gated Schmitt astable with logic-1 gate-on and normally-low output.*

The main drawback of the TTL Schmitt astable is that its low maximum value of timing resistor (1k2) makes it necessary to use large and often very costly $C$ values at low operating frequencies. Suppose, for example, that a design calls for the use of a 1% polystyrene capacitor, to give an edequate degree of precision and thermal stability. The largest readily-available 'decade' size of these is 10nF, and each one costs about 40% more than a single 74LS14 IC and, in a Schmitt astable using a 1k0 timing resistor, gives an operating frequency of about 68kHz. Thus, if you need a 1kHz output you could wire 68 of these capacitors in parallel, to make a Schmitt astable that has a total 'components' cost 96 times greater than that of a single 74LS14 IC. One sensible alternative is to use a single 10nF capacitor to make a precision 100kHz astable, and then divide its output frequency by 100 via two decade counter ICs, as shown in the circuit of *Figure 3.40*, which provides outputs of

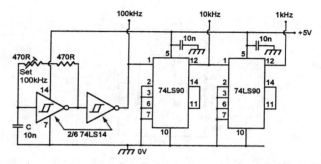

Figure 3.40 *This expanded 100kHz Schmitt astable circuit gives 10kHz and 1kHz outputs.*

100kHz, 10kHz, and 1kHz, and has a total component cost only 9 times greater than a single 74LS14 IC.

The most cost-effective way of generating really good and stable low-frequency high-fan-out TTL-compatible squarewaves is via an ordinary 555-timer IC, connected in its astable mode as shown in the basic circuit of *Figure 3.41*. The standard bipolar version of this IC costs less than a 74LS14, is guaranteed to operate at supply values down to 4.5 volts, and at 5V can use timing resistor values of up to 3.3 megohms; the alternative CMOS version of the device (the 7555) costs 2.5 times more than a single 74LS14 IC, but can use supplies as low as 2V, and at 5V can use timing resistor values of up to 166 megohms. Thus, either type of 555 can be used as a 1kHz astable by using R2–C1 values of 75k–10nF, or 750k–1nF, etc.

For the benefit of those readers who are not already familiar with

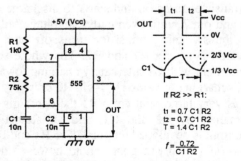

Figure 3.41 *Basic 1kHz 555 astable squarewave generator.*

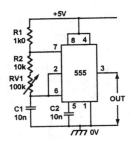

Figure 3.42   *Variable-frequency (650Hz to 7.2kHz) squarewave generator.*

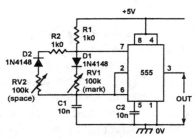

Figure 3.43   *Astable with mark and space periods independently variable from 7μs to 750μs.*

the 555 and the basic circuit in *Figure 3.41,* here is a brief account of the circuit's operation. The 555 IC houses a couple of precision reference-voltage generators and voltage comparators that drive a Set–Reset flip-flop that in turn controls a switching transistor and output driver, etc. When power is first applied to the *Figure 3.41* astable circuit, C1 starts to charge exponentially via the series R1–R2 combination, until eventually its voltage rises to $\frac{2}{3}V_{CC}$, at which point the internal transistor turns on and starts to discharge C1 exponentially via R2 and pin 7, until eventually its voltage falls to $\frac{1}{3}V_{CC}$, at which point the switching transistor turns off and C1 starts to recharge towards $\frac{2}{3}V_{CC}$ via R1 and R2. The whole sequence then repeats *ad infinitum*, with C1 alternately charging towards $\frac{2}{3}V_{CC}$ via R1–R2 and discharging towards $\frac{1}{3}V_{CC}$ via R2 only.

When R2 is very large relative to R1 the operating frequency is determined mainly by R2 and C1, and an almost symmetrical squarewave output is developed on pin 3. The R1 and R2 values can be varied from 1k0 to many megohms; note, however, that R1 affects the circuit's current consumption, since pin 7 is effectively grounded

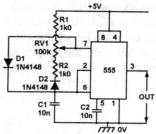

Figure 3.44  *1.2kHz astable with duty-cycle variable from 1% to 99% via RV1.*

during half of each cycle. *Figure 3.42* shows how the operating frequency of the basic circuit can be made variable by replacing R2 with a series-wired fixed and a variable resistor, to give a frequency that is variable from 650Hz to 7.2kHz via RV1; the frequency span can be further increased by selecting alternative values of C1.

*Figure 3.43* shows a circuit variation in which C1 alternately charges up via R1–D1–RV1 and discharges via RV2–D2–R2 in each operating cycle, thus enabling the squarewave's *mark* and *space* periods to be independently varied from 7µs to 750µs via RV1 and RV2 respectively. *Figure 3.44* shows another useful variation, in which C1 alternately charges via R1–D1 and the upper half of RV1 but discharges via D2–R2 and the lower half of RV1, the action being such that the mark period increases as the space period decreases, and *vice versa*, the total period of each cycle being constant. The circuit operates at a nominal 1.2kHz with the C1 value shown, but its duty cycle is fully variable from 1% to 99% via RV1.

Finally, to complete this look at TTL waveform generator circuits, *Figure 3.45* shows how two simple 74LS04 or similar TTL inverter

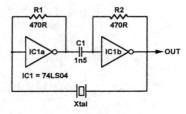

Figure 3.45  *TTL crystal oscillator, for use with series-resonant crystals.*

elements can be used as the basis of a crystal oscillator by biasing them into their linear modes via 470R feedback resistors and then AC coupling them in series via C1, to give zero overall phase shift; the circuit is then made to oscillate by wiring the crystal (which must be a series resonant type) between the output and input as shown. This circuit can operate from a few hundred kHz to above 10MHz.

# 4 Clocked flip-flops and counters

Most digital ICs can be classified into either of two basic types; the first is those based on simple logic gate networks, and many of these have already been described in particular, Chapter 2. The second type is those based on 'clocked' bistable or flip-flop elements, and this group includes simple counter/divider ICs, shift registers, data latches, and complex ICs such as presettable up/down counters, etc. This chapter takes a detailed look at clocked flip-flop basics, and presents practical user information on a variety of popular TTL clocked flip-flop and counter/divider ICs.

## Clocked flip-flop basics

One of the simplest types of digital flip-flop circuit is the cross-coupled NOR-type bistable. This flip-flop has already been briefly described in Chapter 3, but its basic circuit and standard symbol are repeated here in *Figure 4.1*, together with its full Truth Table. The circuit's basic action is such that its Q output switches to logic-1 (and NOT-Q goes to logic-0) when the SET terminal is taken to logic-1,

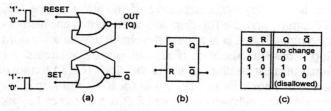

| S | R | Q | $\bar{Q}$ |
|---|---|---|---|
| 0 | 0 | no change | |
| 0 | 1 | 0 | 1 |
| 1 | 0 | 1 | 0 |
| 1 | 1 | 0 | 0 |
| | | (disallowed) | |

(a)  (b)  (c)

Figure 4.1  *Circuit (a), symbol (b), and Truth Table of the NOR-type S–R flip-flop.*

and then latches into that state even if SET and RESET are both then pulled to logic-0. The only way that the latched output states can be changed is to apply a logic-1 to the RESET terminal, in which case the Q output switches to logic-0 and latches into that state even if SET and RESET are both then pulled to logic-0. The basic SET–RESET (S–R, or R–S) flip-flop thus acts as a simple memory element that 'remembers' which of the two inputs last went to logic-1. Note that if both inputs go to logic-1 simultaneously, both outputs go to logic-0, but if both inputs then simultaneously switch to logic-0 the output states cannot be predicted; the 'both inputs high' condition is thus regarded as a 'disallowed' state.

Note at this point that the S–R bistable is actually a Schmitt-like voltage-triggered regenerative switch; the NOR-type circuit triggers when its input (SET or RESET) voltage *rises* to some intermediate value between the logic-0 and logic-1 levels at which the TTL input stage is biased into its linear amplifying mode; a NAND-type circuit triggers when the input voltage *falls* to some intermediate value. Thus, all NOR-type bistable circuits are intrinsically 'level-sensitive, rising-edge triggered' elements, and NAND-type bistable circuits are intrinsically 'level-sensitive, falling-edge triggered' elements; these basic expressions are now part of popular flip-flop jargon.

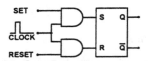

Figure 4.2   *Basic circuit of a clocked R-S flip-flop.*

The versatility of the basic S-R flip-flop can be greatly enhanced by wiring a 2-input AND gate in series with each input terminal, as shown in *Figure 4.2*, so that logic-1 input signals can only reach the S–R flip-flop when the 'clock' or trigger signal is also at logic-1. Thus, when the clock signal is at logic-0, both inputs of the S–R flip-flop are held at logic-0, irrespective of the states of the SET and RESET inputs, and the flip-flop acts as a permanent memory, but when the clock signal is at logic-1 the circuit acts as a standard S–R flip-flop. Consequently, data is not automatically latched into the flip-flop, but must be clocked in via the clock (CLK) terminal; this circuit is thus known as a clocked S-R (or R–S) flip-flop.

*Figure 4.3* shows how two clocked S-R flip-flops can be cascaded and clocked in anti-phase (via an inverter in the clock line) to make

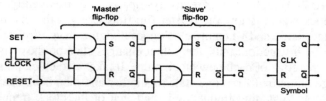

Figure 4.3 *Clocked master–slave flip-flop basic circuit and symbol.*

one of the most important of all flip-flop elements, the clocked master–slave flip-flop. The basic action of this circuit is as follows.

## The master–slave flip-flop

When the clock input terminal of the *Figure 4.3* circuit is in the low state the inputs to the 'master' flip-flop are enabled via the inverter, so the SET–RESET data is accepted, but the inputs to the 'slave' flip-flop are disabled, so this data is not passed to the output terminals. When the clock input terminal goes to the high state the inputs to the master flip-flop are disabled via the inverter, which thus outputs only the remembered input data, and simultaneously the input to the slave flip-flop is enabled and the remembered data is latched and passed to the output terminals. Thus, the clocked master–slave flip-flop accepts input data or information only when the clock signal is low, and passes that data to the output on the arrival of the rising-edge of the clock signal, i.e. its data-shifting action is synchronous with the timing of the clock signal. This flip-flop uses the circuit symbol shown in the diagram.

The clocked master–slave flip-flop can be made to give a clocked toggle or divide-by-2 action by cross-coupling its input and output terminals as shown in *Figure 4.4*, so that SET and Q (and RESET

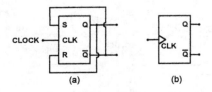

Figure 4.4 *A clocked 'toggle' or 'T-type' flip-flop is constructed as shown in (a), and uses the standard symbol of (b).*

and NOT-Q) logic levels are always opposite. Consequently, when the clock signal is low the master flip-flop receives the instruction 'change state', and when the clock goes high the slave flip-flop executes the instruction; thus, the output changes state on the arrival of the rising-edge of each new clock pulse. It takes two clock pulses to change the output from one state to another and then back again, so the output switching frequency is half that of the clock frequency. This circuit, which is known as a 'toggle' or 'T-type' flip-flop, thus acts as a binary divide-by-2 'counter'.

*Figure 4.4b* shows the basic circuit symbol of the clocked T-type flip-flop; note that the sharp-edged 'notch' symbol on the CLK input indicates that the element (the flip-flop) is 'triggered' by the rising-edge of a clock signal (falling-edge triggering can be notated by adding a 'little circle' symbol to the CLK line).

## D and JK flip-flops

The T-type flip-flop is a specialized element that acts purely as a counter/divider. A far more versatile device is the 'data' or 'D-type' flip-flop, which is made by connecting the clocked master–slave flip-flop as shown in *Figure 4.5*. Here, an inverter is wired between the S and R terminals of the flip-flop, so that these terminals are always in anti-phase and the input data is applied via a single data terminal. *Figures 4.5b* and *c* show the symbol and Truth Table of the D-type flip-flop, which can be used as a data latch by using the connections

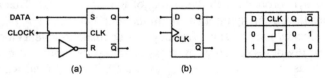

Figure 4.5   *Basic circuit (a), symbol (b), and Truth Table of the D-type flip-top.*

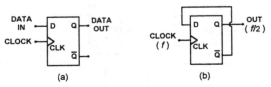

Figure 4.6   *A D-type flip-flop can be used as (a) a data latch or (b) as a divide-by-2 (binary counter/divider) circuit.*

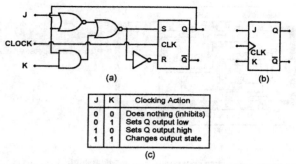

(a)                                                (b)

| J | K | Clocking Action |
|---|---|---|
| 0 | 0 | Does nothing (inhibits) |
| 0 | 1 | Sets Q output low |
| 1 | 0 | Sets Q output high |
| 1 | 1 | Changes output state |

(c)

Figure 4.7   *Basic circuit (a), symbol (b), and action table of the JK flip-flop.*

shown in *Figure 4.6a*, or as a binary counter/divider by using the connections shown in *Figure 4.6b*, where the D and NOT-Q terminals are shorted together.

Note in the *Figure 4.5* Truth Table that the 'rising step' symbol used in the CLK (clock) column is a standard symbol that indicates that the circuit element (the flip-flop) triggers or changes state on the arrival of a clock signal's rising-edge; a 'falling step' symbol can be used to indicate that an element triggers in the arrival of a clock signal's falling-edge.

*Figure 4.7* shows the basic circuit, symbol and action table of the most important and versatile of all clocked flip-flops, the JK type, which can be 'programmed' to act as either a data latch, a counter/divider, or a do-nothing element by suitably connecting the J and K terminals as indicated in the table. In essence, the JK flip-flop acts like a T-type when the J and K terminals are both high, or as a D-type when the J and K terminals are at different logic levels. When the J and K terminals are both low the flip-flop states remain unchanged on the arrival of a clock pulse. Note that clocked T-type, D-type, and JK flip-flops all give a synchronous or clock-synchronized switching action.

## The 74LS74 D-type flip-flop IC

The best known D-type TTL flip-flop IC is the 74LS74. This is a 'Dual' IC, containing two independent D-type flip-flops that share common power supply connections; Figure 4.8 shows the functional diagram and pin notations of this IC, together with its Truth Tables.

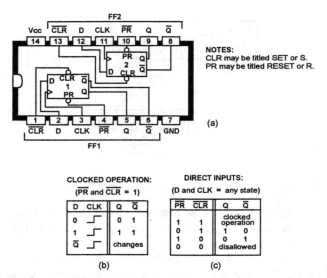

NOTES:
CLR may be titled SET or S.
PR may be titled RESET or R.

(a)

CLOCKED OPERATION:
(PR and CLR = 1)

| D | CLK | Q | Q̄ |
|---|-----|---|----|
| 0 | ⎍ | 0 | 1 |
| 1 | ⎍ | 1 | 1 |
| Q̄ | ⎍ | changes | |

(b)

DIRECT INPUTS:
(D and CLK = any state)

| PR | CLR | Q | Q̄ |
|----|-----|---|----|
| 1 | 1 | clocked operation | |
| 0 | 1 | 1 | 0 |
| 1 | 0 | 0 | 1 |
| 0 | 0 | disallowed | |

(c)

Figure 4.8   *Functional diagram and Truth Tables of the 74LS74 Dual D-type flip-flop IC.*

Before looking at ways of using this IC, it is worth while spending a few moments considering the general symbology, etc., used in this and other flip-flop diagrams, as follows.

Note in the functional diagram *Figure 4.8a* that each flip-flop element has inputs that are internally notated PR and CLR, and that the feed-ins to these points carry little negation circles, indicating that PR and CLR are active-low; consequently, the actual IC pins that connect to these points should correctly be notated $\overline{PR}$ and $\overline{CLR}$ (NOT-PR and NOT-CLR) to indicate their active-low actions. The terms PR and CLR are actually abbreviations for PRESET and CLEAR, and are favoured by most manufacturers of flip-flop ICs, but – as is shown in Truth Table (*Figure 4.8c*) – they give the same direct control of the Q and NOT-Q output states as conventional SET

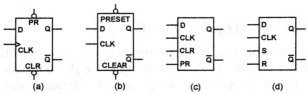

Figure 4.9   *Four common variations of the 74LS74 D-type flip-flop symbol.*

and RESET signals, and these latter terms are preferred by a few manufacturers.

*Figure 4.9* shows four common variations of the 74LS74 D-type flip-flop symbol. *Figure 4.9a* diagram states that the flip-flop uses rising-edge clocking and negated PR and CLR control, etc., and is an excellent 'data sheet' diagram; but all D-type flip-flops are edge-triggered, and the PR and CLR notations are a bit ambiguous, so *Figure 4.9b* is equally good. The symbols in *Figures 4.9a* and *b* are both too complex for general circuit-diagram use, and can be simplified by eliminating their negation circles, etc., and abbreviating and perhaps repositioning their PRESET/CLEAR or SET/RESET titles, as shown in the examples of *Figures 4.9c* and *d*.

Turning now to ways of using the 74LS74 or similar D-type flip-

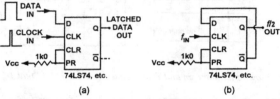

(a)  (b)

Figure 4.10   *A Data latch (a) and a divide-by-2 counter (b) made from a 74LS74 or similar D-type flip-flop.*

flop elements, note from the Truth Table in *Figure 4.8c* that $\overline{PR}$ and $\overline{CLR}$ must be tied high (to logic-1) to give normal clocked operation, and from the Truth Table in *Figure 4.8b* that the element can be used as a Data latch by feeding Data to the D terminal, or as a divide-by-2 counter by shorting the D and NOT-Q terminals together. *Figure 4.10* shows the 74LS74 circuit connections used in these two modes of operation; in the Data latch (*Figure 4.10a*) mode the 'D' logic-level is latched into the flip-flop and presented at its Q output by the rising-edge of a clock pulse, and is then retained until another clock pulse arrives; in the 'counter' mode, the Q output frequency is precisely half that of the clock signal.

## The 74LS73 JK-type flip flop IC

The best known JK-type TTL flip-flop IC is the 74LS73. This is a 'Dual' IC, containing two independent JK flip-flops that share common power supply connections; *Figure 4.11* shows the functional diagram and pin notations of this IC, together with its Truth Tables. Note that it has unusual supply-pin connections, with pin 4

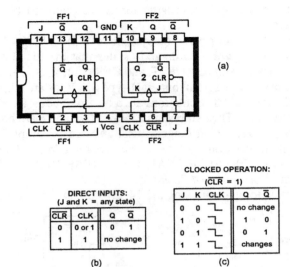

(a)

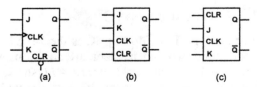

DIRECT INPUTS:
(J and K = any state)

| $\overline{CLR}$ | CLK | Q | $\overline{Q}$ |
|---|---|---|---|
| 0 | 0 or 1 | 0 | 1 |
| 1 | 1 | no change | |

(b)

CLOCKED OPERATION:
($\overline{CLR}$ = 1)

| J | K | CLK | Q | $\overline{Q}$ |
|---|---|---|---|---|
| 0 | 0 | ⌐_ | no change | |
| 1 | 0 | ⌐_ | 1 | 0 |
| 0 | 1 | ⌐_ | 0 | 1 |
| 1 | 1 | ⌐_ | changes | |

(c)

Figure 4.11   *Functional diagram and Truth Tables of the 74LS73 Dual JK flip-flop IC.*

acting as $V_{CC}$ and pin 11 as GND. Also note that, like most TTL JK flip-flops, it uses negative-edge triggering, as indicated by the little negation circle on the clock input of each flip-flop symbol. Each flip-flop has a negated CLR (CLEAR) terminal, which is normally biased to logic-1; when CLR is pulled to logic-0 it sets the Q output to logic-0. *Figure 4.12* shows three variations of the 74LS73 JK flip-flop symbol: *Figure 4.12a* is a strictly-correct 'Data Sheet' type of symbol, and *Figures 4.12b* and *c* are simplified versions suitable for use in circuit diagrams, for example.

*Figure 4.13* shows two basic ways of using a 74LS73 JK flip-flop element. It can be used as a binary divide-by-2 circuit by tying its CLR and J and K terminals to logic-1 via a shared bias resistor and feeding the input signal to the CLK terminal, as shown in *Figure 4.13a*. Alternatively, it can be used as a Data latch by biasing CLR

Figure 4.12   *Strictly-correct (a) and common variations (b) and (c) of the 74LS73 JK flip-flop symbol.*

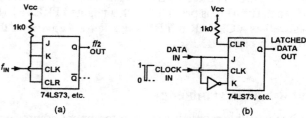

Figure 4.13 *A divide-by-2 circuit (a) and a Data latch (b) made from a 74LS73 or similar JK flip-flop.*

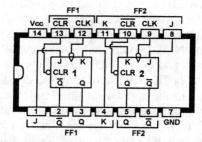

Figure 4.14 *Functional diagram of the 74LS107 Dual JK flip-flop IC.*

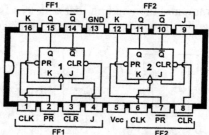

Figure 4.15 *Functional diagram of the 74LS76 Dual JK flip-flop IC with PRESET and CLEAR.*

to logic-1, feeding the Data in direct form to J and inverted form to K, and using a negative-going pulse to latch the data in, as shown in *Figure 4.13b* (note that the Standard '7473' version of this IC differs slightly, and is triggered by the falling-edge of a positive pulse).

There are two useful variations of the basic 74LS73 IC. One of these is the 74LS107, which is internally identical to the 74LS73 but has more conventional pin allocations, with pin 7 acting as GND, and pin 14 as $V_{CC}$; *Figure 4.14* shows this IC's functional diagram.

The other variation is the 74LS76, which uses a 16-pin IC package in which each flip-flop is provided with a negated PRESET (PR) terminal as well as a CLEAR (CLR) one; *Figure 4.15* shows the functional diagram of this IC.

## Circuit diagram symbology

It is pertinent at this moment to note a few more points concerning logic symbology, as applicable to clocked flip-flops and circuit diagrams. Broadly speaking, any logic-circuit diagram can be presented in either a generalized form, using greatly simplified circuit symbols, or in a specific form, using accurate circuit symbols that apply to specific ICs, etc. Thus, all D-type flip-flops have D and CLK input terminals and Q and NOT-Q output terminals, and all JK types have J, K and CLK inputs and Q and NOT-Q outputs, so the basic ways of using *any* D-type or JK-type flip-flop in the divide-by-two mode can be presented as in the general or 'universal' circuit diagram of *Figure 4.16*. If an engineer wants to build either of these circuits from a specific IC of the appropriate type, he or she can do so by simply looking up that IC Data Sheet or Truth Table to find the appropriate connections for any terminals that are not mentioned in the general diagram, and then adding that data to a 'specific' circuit diagram, as shown in the examples of *Figures 4.17* and *4.18*.

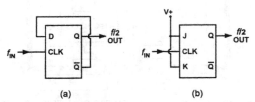

(a)                                 (b)

Figure 4.16   *General circuit diagrams of (a) D-type and (b) JK divide-by-2 stages.*

The two circuits in *Figure 4.17* are based on 4000-series CMOS ICs; the 4013B is a Dual D-type IC in which each flip-flop has active-high SET (S) and RESET (R) terminals, which can be disabled by tying them directly to ground, as in *Figure 4.17a*. The 4027B is a Dual JK-type IC with active-high SET and RESET terminals that can be disabled by grounding them, and with J and K terminals that can be put into the logic-1 state by tying them directly to the $V_{CC}$ line, as shown in *Figure 4.17b*. The circuits in *Figure 4.18*

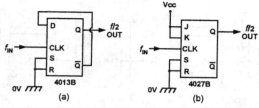

Figure 4.17 *Specific circuit diagrams for 4000-series CMOS (a) D-type and (b) JK-type divide-by-2 stages.*

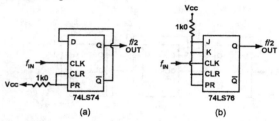

Figure 4.18 *Specific circuit diagrams for 74LS-series (a) D-type and (b) JK-type divide-by-2 stages.*

are based on 74LS-series TTL ICs; the circuit in *Figure 4.18a* uses a 74LS74 Dual D-type IC, and has already been described; the design in *Figure 4.18b* uses a 74LS76 Dual JK-type IC, and its CLR and PR terminals are disabled by tying them to the $V_{CC}$ line via a shared 1k0 resistor, as shown.

Thus, 'general' logic-circuit diagrams are a useful way of presenting valuable design information, and can easily be translated into 'specific' circuit diagram form. Several 'general' logic-circuit diagrams are used in the remaining sections of this chapter.

# Ripple counters

The most popular application of the TTL clocked flip-flop is as a binary counter, and the reader has already seen in *Figure 4.18* how individual D-type and JK-type elements can be used to give divide-by-2 action in this mode; when these circuits are clocked by a fixed-frequency waveform they give a symmetrical squarewave output at half of the clock frequency.

Numbers of basic divide-by-2 stages can be cascaded to give multiple binary division by simply clocking each new stage from the appropriate output of the preceding stage. Thus, *Figure 4.19* shows

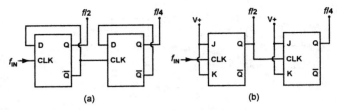

Figure 4.19  *General circuit diagram of (a) D-type and (b) JK divide-by-4 ripple counters.*

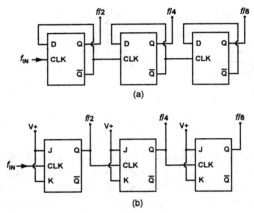

Figure 4.20  *General circuit diagram of (a) D-type and (b) JK divide-by-8 ripple counters.*

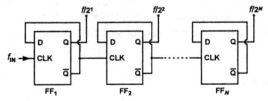

Figure 4.21  *General circuit diagram of a D-type divide-by-$N^2$ ripple counter.*

(in 'general' form) how two D or JK stages can be cascaded to give an overall division ratio of four ($2^2$), and *Figure 4.20* shows how three stages can be cascaded to give a division ratio of eight ($2^3$). *Figure 4.21* shows how D-type stages can be cascaded to make a divide-by-$2^N$ counter, where $N$ is the number of counter stages. Thus, four stages give a ratio of 16 ($2^4$), five stages give 32 ($2^5$), six give 64 ($2^6$), and so on. In modern flip-flip jargon, the number of stages in a multi-stage binary divider are often referred to as its 'bit' size; thus, a four-stage counter may be called a '4-bit' counter, or an eight-stage counter an 8-bit counter, and so on. The multi-bit circuits in *Figures 4.19* to *4.21* are known as ripple dividers (or counters), because each stage is clocked by a preceding stage (rather than directly by the input clock signal), and the clock signal thus seems to ripple through the dividers. Inevitably, the propagation delays of the individual dividers all add together to give a summed delay at the end of the chain, and counter stages other than the first thus do not clock in precise synchrony with the original clock signal; such counters are thus described as 'asynchronous' in action.

If the multi-bit outputs of a ripple divider/counter are decoded via gate networks, the propagation delays of the asynchronous dividers can result in unwanted output 'glitches' (see the 'Decoding' section later in this chapter), so ripple counters are best used in straight-forward frequency-divider applications, where no decoding is required. These applications may range in complexity from simple 2-bit 'divide-by-4' types, to ones using 22 or more divider stages. *Figures 4.22* to *4.24* show some common applications of large-bit ripple dividers.

In *Figure 4.22* a 'top-C' (4186.0Hz) generator is used in conjunction with a 7-bit ripple divider to make an 8-octave 'C' note generator that produces symmetrical squarewave output on terminals C1 to C7; this basic type of circuit is widely used in electronic pianos,

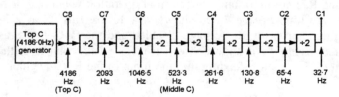

Figure 4.22 *A 7-bit ripple divider used to make an 8-octave 'C'-note generator.*

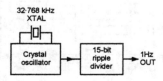

Figure 4.23 *Timing generator circuit commonly used in digital watches.*

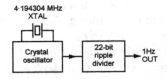

**Figure 4.24**   *Timing generator circuit using a commonly-available crystal reference.*

for example. *Figure 4.23* shows a 15-bit ripple divider and a 32.768kHz crystal oscillator used to made a precision 1Hz timing generator of the type that is commonly used in digital watches, and *Figure 4.24* uses a 22-bit ripple divider and a commonly available 4.194304MHz crystal reference, etc., to make another precision 1Hz generator.

### Large-bit ripple divider ICs.

74LS73, 74LS74 and similar 'Dual' flip-flop ICs can be cascaded to give any desired number of ripple stages, but where more than four stages are needed it is invariably more economic to use special-purpose MSI ripple-counter ICs. *Figure 4.25* shows one popular but rather expensive IC of this type, the 74LS93 4-bit JK ripple counter/divider, in which the four dividers are arranged in 1-bit plus 3-bit style and share a common 2-input AND gated RESET line that puts all four outputs (A, B, C, D) into the '0' state when both inputs (R1 and R2) are high, but gives normal operation when one or both inputs are low. *Figure 4.26a* shows how to use this IC as a 3-bit ripple counter, with the A stage disabled and the B–C–D stages in use, and *Figure 4.26b* shows how to use it as a 4-bit counter, with the output of the A stage feeding into the input of the B–C–D chain.

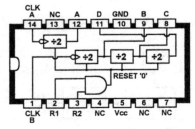

Figure 4.25   *Functional diagram of the 74LS93 4-bit JK ripple counter/divider IC.*

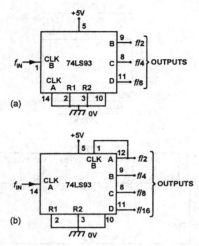

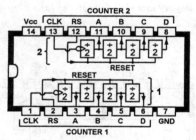

Figure 4.26  *Connections for using the 74LS93 as (a) a 3-bit or (b) 4-bit ripple counter/divider.*

Figure 4.27  *Functional diagram of the 74LS393 Dual 4-bit ripple counter/divider IC.*

*Figure 4.27* shows the functional diagram of a far more economic IC, which (at the time of writing) costs half the price of the 74LS93 but has double the bit count. This is the 74LS393 Dual 4-bit ripple counter IC, in which each 4-bit counter has its own CLOCK and RESET (RS) input pins; the RESET line puts all four outputs (A, B, C, D) into the '0' state when the RS input is high, but gives normal ripple-count operation when RS is low. *Figure 4.28a* shows how to use this IC as a 1- to 4-bit ripple counter, with the '1' counter in use and the '2' counter disabled, and (b) shows how to use it as a 1- to 8-bit counter, with both counters in use.

If you need a ripple counter with a bit-count greater than eight, one attractive option is to use a dedicated CMOS IC for the purpose.

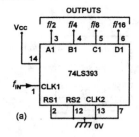

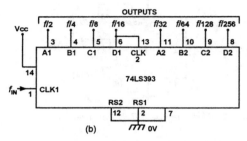

Figure 4.28   *Basic ways of using the 74LS393 as (a) a 1- to 4-bit circuit, or (b) a 1- to 8-bit circuit.*

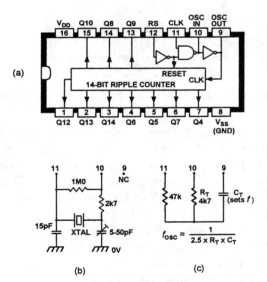

Figure 4.29   *Functional diagram (a) of the 4060B/74HC4060 14-bit ripple counter, with connections for using its internal gates as (b) a crystal oscillator or (c) R–C oscillator.*

Three noteworthy specimens are readily available, at low cost, in 4000B-series and/or 74HC-series versions. Of these, the 4040B/74HC4040 is a 12-bit ripple counter with all twelve outputs externally available, and the 4020B is 14-bit ripple counter with all but bits 2 and 3 externally available. The most interesting of the trio is the 4060B/74HC4060, which is a 14-bit ripple counter with all but bits 1, 2, 3 and 11 externally available, and which can be clocked via either an external signal or via a built-in clock oscillator circuit. *Figure 4.29* shows the functional diagram of the 4060B/74HC4060 IC, together with the connections for using its internal circuit as either a crystal or an R–C oscillator (if an external clock signal is to be used, apply it directly to pin 11, and leave pins 9 and 10 open). Of the two IC versions, the 74HC4060 is the best for TTL-compatible use as each output terminal has an LS fan-out of 10 and the IC has a typical maximum clocking frequency of about 70MHz.

## Output decoding

The outputs of a 2-stage divide-by-4 ripple counter have, as shown in *Figure 4.30a* and *b*, four possible binary states. Thus, at the start or '0' reference point of each clocking cycle the Q2 and Q1 outputs are both in the logic-0 state. On the arrival of the first clock pulse in the cycle, Q1 switches high. On the arrival of the second pulse, Q2 goes high and Q1 goes low. On the third pulse, Q2 and Q1 both go high. Finally, on the arrival of the fourth pulse Q2 and Q1 both go low again, and the cycle is back to its original '0' reference state.

Each of the four possible binary states of the ripple counter can be decoded, to give four unique outputs, by ANDing the logic-1 outputs that are unique to each one of the states, using the AND-gate connections shown in *Figure 4.30c*. Since the ripple counter is an asynchronous device, however, the propagation delay between the two flip-flips may cause 'glitches' to appear in some decoded outputs, as in the example of the decoded-'0' waveforms shown in *Figure 4.30d*.

The principles outlined in *Figure 4.30* can be extended to any multi-stage ripple counters in which all significant binary outputs are accessible for decoding. Note, however, that the greater the number of stages, the greater the total propagation delays and, consequently, the greater the magnitude (width) of any decoded glitches. For

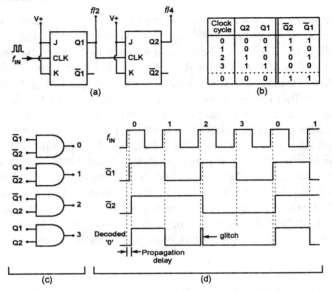

Figure 4.30 *Circuit (a) and binary output states (b) of a 2-stage ripple counter. Each of the four possible binary states can be decoded via a 2-input AND gate (c), but the decoded outputs may not be glitch-free, as shown in the decoded-'0' example in (d).*

example, a single 74LS-series JK or D-type flip-flop has a typical propagation delay of 20ns (0.02μs), so if the 2-stage circuit in *Figure 4.30* is operating at a clock frequency of 1MHz (period = 1μs), the glitch width equals a trivial 2% of a clock cycle, but in a 20-stage divider the glitch width may equal a massive 38% of a clock cycle, etc.

## Walking-ring counters

Ripple counters are very useful where simple binary division is needed but, as already explained, are subject to glitch problems that debar them from some sensitive decoded-counting applications. Fortunately, an alternative binary division technique is available that is well suited to the latter type of application; it is known as the walking-ring technique. In this technique, numbers of flip-flops (usually JK types) are clocked in parallel and thus operate in synchrony with the input clock signal, and digital feedback determines how each stage will react to individual clock pulses; such counters

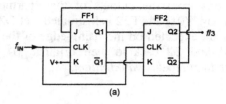

(a)

| Clock cycle | Q2 | Q1 | FF2 JK code | | FF2 Instruction | FF1 JK code | | FF1 Instruction |
|---|---|---|---|---|---|---|---|---|
| ⊓ 0 | 0 | 0 | 0 | 1 | Set Q2 low | 1 | 1 | change state |
| ⌐ 1 | 0 | 1 | | | | | | |
| ⊓ 1 | 0 | 1 | 1 | 0 | Set Q2 high | 1 | 1 | change state |
| ⌐ 2 | 1 | 0 | | | | | | |
| ⊓ 2 | 1 | 0 | 0 | 1 | Set Q2 low | 0 | 1 | Set Q1 low |
| ⌐ 0 | 0 | 0 | | | | | | |

(b)

Figure 4.31   *Circuit (a) and Truth Table of a synchronous divide-by-3 counter.*

are known as synchronous types, and they give glitch-free decoded outputs.

The 'JK' version of the walking-ring technique depends on the fact that any JK flip-flop can be 'programmed' via its J and K terminals to act as either a SET or RESET latch, a binary divider, or as a do-nothing device. A detailed example of the basic walking-ring technique is given in *Figure 4.31*, which shows the circuit and Truth Tables of a synchronous divide-by-3 counter. Note that the Truth Table shows the action state of each flip-flop at each stage of the counting cycle; remember that when the clock is low the action instruction is loaded (via the J and K terminals) into the flip-flop, and the instruction is then carried out as the clock signal transitions high.

Thus at the start of the cycle (clock low), when Q2 and Q1 are both low the binary instruction 'change state' (11) is loaded into FF1 via its J and K terminals, and the instruction 'set Q2 low' (01) is loaded into FF2. On the arrival of the first clock pulse this instruction is executed, and Q1 goes high and Q2 stays low.

When the clock goes low again, new program information is fed to the flip-flops. FF1 is instructed to 'change state' (11) and FF2 is instructed 'set Q2 high' (10); these instructions are executed on the rising-edge of the second clock pulse, causing Q2 to go high and Q1 to go low.

When the clock goes low again new program information is again fed to the flip-flops from the outputs of their partners. FF1 is instructed 'set Q1 low' (01) and FF2 is instructed 'set Q2 low' (01); these instructions are executed on the rising-edge of the next clock pulse, driving Q1 and Q2 back to their original '0' states. The counting sequence then repeats *ad infinitum*.

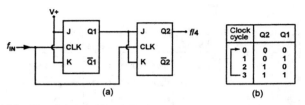

| Clock cycle | Q2 | Q1 |
|---|---|---|
| 0 | 0 | 0 |
| 1 | 0 | 1 |
| 2 | 1 | 0 |
| 3 | 1 | 1 |

(a)    (b)

Figure 4.32   *Circuit (a) and Truth Table (b) of a synchronous divide-by-4 counter.*

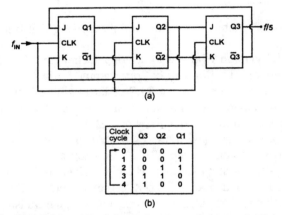

| Clock cycle | Q3 | Q2 | Q1 |
|---|---|---|---|
| 0 | 0 | 0 | 0 |
| 1 | 0 | 0 | 1 |
| 2 | 0 | 1 | 1 |
| 3 | 1 | 1 | 0 |
| 4 | 1 | 0 | 0 |

(b)

Figure 4.33   *Circuit (a) and Truth Table (b) of a synchronous divide-by-5 counter.*

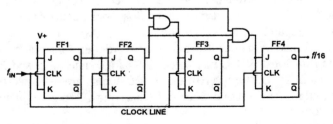

Figure 4.34   *Circuit of a synchronous divide-by-16 counter.*

Thus, in the walking-ring counter all flip-flips are clocked in parallel, but are cross-coupled so that the clocking response of any one stage depends on the states of the other stages. Walking-ring counters can be configured to give any desired count ratio, and *Figures 4.32* and *4.33* show the circuits and Truth Tables of divide-by-4 and divide-by-5 counters respectively. In some cases, circuit operation relies on cross-coupling via AND gates, etc., and an example of this is shown in the four-stage divide-by-16 counter of *Figure 4.34*. In walking-ring counters based on D-type flip-flops, cross-coupling may be made to the SET or RESET terminals of individual flip-flop stages, etc.

## The 'Johnson' counter

One useful variation of the synchronous walking-ring counter is a circuit known as the 'Johnson' counter, which is really a closed-loop version of a circuit known as a 'bucket brigade' synchronous data shifter. *Figure 4.35* shows a basic bucket brigade circuit; note that it is shown built from parallel-clocked cascaded D-type flip-flops, and

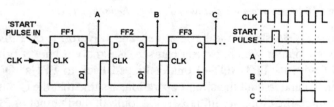

Figure 4.35   *Circuit and waveforms of a basic bucket brigade synchronous data shifter.*

remember that these flip-flops latch the 'D'-terminal data (logic-state) into 'Q' on the arrival of the rising-edge of a clock pulse. Thus, if all flip-flop outputs are initially in the logic-0 state, output A latches into the logic-1 state for one full clock cycle if a brief edge-straddling 'start' pulse is fed to FF1 at the start of that cycle, as shown. At the start of the next clock cycle the A waveform latches into FF2 and appears at output B, and in the next cycle it shifts down to C, and so on down the line for as many flip-flop stages as there are, until it is eventually clocked out of the circuit. Thus, the initial 'A' waveform passed through the circuit one step at a time, bucket-brigade style, in synchrony with the clock signal.

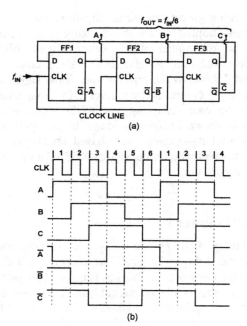

Figure 4.36   *Circuit and waveforms of a 3-stage Johnson counter.*

*Figure 4.36* shows the basic circuit and waveforms of a 3-stage Johnson counter which, as you can see, is simply a bucket brigade circuit with its FF3 NOT-Q output looped back to FF1's 'D' terminal. To understand the circuit operation, assume that the Q outputs of all three flip-flops are initially set at logic-0; the D input of FF1 is thus at logic-1. On the arrival of CP1 (clock pulse 1) output A latches high, and B and C remain low. On the arrival of CP2 the NOT-Q output of FF3 is still high, so output A remains in the high state, but output B is also latched high. On the arrival of CP3 the NOT-Q output of FF3 is still high, so outputs A and B remain high, but output C is also latched high. Consequently, on the arrival of CP4 the NOT-Q output of FF3 is low, so output A latches into the low state, but outputs B and C remain high. This process continues, as shown by the waveforms in *Figure 4.36*, until the end of CP6, and a new sequencing process then starts on the arrival of the next clock pulse.

There are several important features to note about the basic Johnson counter circuit of *Figure 4.36*. First, note that a complete operating cycle takes six clock pulses (i.e. twice the number of flip-

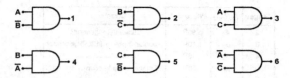

Figure 4.37 *Clock-cycle decoding networks for use with the circuit of Figure 4.36.*

flop stages), and that the output waveform taken from any one of the six available output points (A, B, C, etc.) is a symmetrical squarewave with an operating frequency of $f_{IN}/6$. Next, note that if the A output waveform is taken as a reference point, all other output waveforms are effectively phase-shifted by 360/6 = 60 degrees relative to A. Finally, note that the outputs of the circuit can be decoded via a 2-input AND gate to give a logic-1 output for the duration of any specific clock cycle by using the connections shown in *Figure 4.37*; thus, to decode CP3, simply AND outputs A and C, or to decode CP5 simply AND C and NOT-B, and so on.

The circuit in *Figure 4.36* is shown built from three D-type flip-flop stages, but in practice a standard Johnson counter can be built from either D-type or JK flop-flops, can have any desired number of stages, and gives output frequency and phase shift magnitudes that are directly related to the total number of flip-flop stages. *Figure*

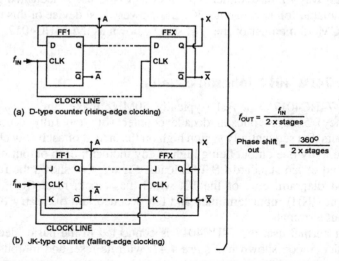

Figure 4.38 *Basic D-type and JK versions of the Johnson counter, with formulae.*

| Stages | $f_{IN}/f_{OUT}$ | Phase shift | Comments |
|--------|------|------|----------|
| 2 | 4 | 90° | 'Quadrature' generator |
| 3 | 6 | 60° | Popular '3-phase' (120°) generator |
| 4 | 8 | 45° | |
| 5 | 10 | 36° | Popular 'decade counter' format |
| 6 | 12 | 30° | |

Figure 4.39  *Basic performance details of some standard Johnson counter circuits.*

*4.38* shows the basic form of the two types of circuit, together with the basic formula that is common to both circuits, and *Figure 4.39* lists the basic performance details of various 'standard' Johnson counter circuits. Note from *Figure 4.39* that the 2-stage circuit is sometimes called a 'quadrature' generator, since it gives four outputs that are phase-shifted by 90 degrees relative to each other, and that the 3-stage circuit (see *Figure 4.36*) can be used as a 3-phase (120 degree phase shift) squarewave generator by taking outputs from A, C and NOT-B. The 5-stage circuit is widely used as a synchronous decade counter/divider.

All the Johnson counter circuits listed in *Figure 4.39* give even values of frequency division (4, 6, 8, etc.), but such counters can also be made to give odd division values by varying their feedback connections, as has already been shown in the divide-by-3 and divide-by-5 examples of *Figures 4.31* and *4.33*. In practice, however, the easiest way to make either type of circuit is to use a dedicated programmable Johnson counter IC, and the very best device of this type is a CMOS member of the '74' series known as the 74HC4017.

## The 74HC4017 Johnson counter

The 74HC4017 is a fast (typically 50MHz maximum clock frequency) 5-stage Johnson decade counter with ten fully decoded outputs that sequentially switch high on the arrival of each new clock pulse, only one output being high at any moment; each output has a fan-out of ten standard LS TTL loads. *Figure 4.40* shows the functional diagram, etc., of the IC, which has clock, reset (RS), and inhibit (INH) input terminals and ten decoded and one carry (CO) output terminals.

In normal use, the 74HC4017 is connected in the basic 'decade divider' mode shown in *Figure 4.41*, with its reset and inhibit terminals grounded. In this mode the IC's Johnson counter stages

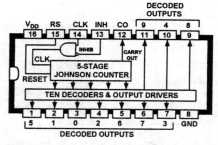

Figure 4.40  *Functional diagram of the 74HC4017 Johnson decade counter with ten decoded outputs.*

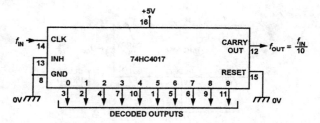

Figure 4.41  *Basic connections for using the 74HC4017 as a rising-edge triggered synchronous decade divider.*

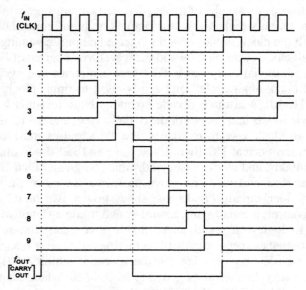

Figure 4.42  *Waveform timing diagram of the circuit of Figure 4.41.*

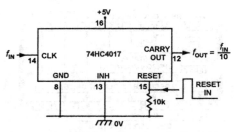

Figure 4.43  *Basic way of using the 74HC4017's RESET terminal.*

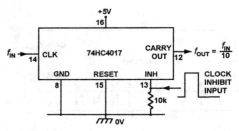

Figure 4.44  *Basic way of using the 74HC4017's CLOCK INHIBIT terminal.*

advance one step on the arrival of each new clock pulse rising-edge and simultaneously set one of the ten decoded outputs high while the other nine outputs remain low; the outputs go high sequentially, in phase with the clock signal, with the selected output remaining high for one full clock cycle, as shown in the waveform diagram of *Figure 4.42*. An additional carry out (CO) signal completes one cycle for every ten clock input cycles, and can be used to ripple-clock additional 74HC4017s in multi-decade counters. Note that this IC has buffer-style inputs that are not of the Schmitt type, and the IC is thus sensitive to clock waveform shapes; the clock pulses must switch fully between normal HC logic-levels, rise and fall times must be less than 400ns, and clock pulse widths must be greater than 15ns.

*Figures 4.43* and *4.44* show two useful variations of the basic 'decade divider' circuit. *Figure 4.43* shows how to use the IC's pin-15 reset control; normally this control is tied to logic-0, but when it is taken to logic-1 it resets all of the IC's counters and sets all decoded outputs except output '0' to the logic-0 state. *Figure 4.44* shows the basic way of using the pin-13 clock inhibit (INH) terminal; normally, this terminal is tied to logic-0, but when it is taken to logic-1 it fully inhibits the IC's clocking and counting actions.

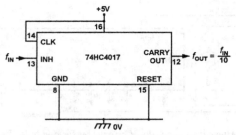

Figure 4.45   *Basic way of using the Philips 74HC4017 to give falling-edge clock triggering (see text).*

There are sometimes minor architectural differences between different manufacturer's versions of the 74HC4017, and in the Philips/Mullard version these enable the device to be triggered by the rising-edges of clock signals by using the connections shown in *Figure 4.41*, or by falling-edges by using the connections of *Figure 4.45*, in which the CLK (pin 14) terminal is tied to logic-1 and the clock signal is fed to the INH (pin 13) terminal (in practice, this configuration works well with most versions of the 74HC4017).

*Figures 4.46* and *4.47* show ways of using the 74HC4017 as a divide-by-$N$ counter with $N$ decoded outputs, in which $N$ = any whole number from 2 to 9. In the circuit in *Figure 4.46* the $N$th decoded output is simply shorted to the reset terminal so that the counter resets to zero on the arrival of the $N$th clock pulse. This circuit is slightly sensitive to the clock signal's pulse width and rise time; the version of the counter shown in *Figure 4.47* does not suffer from this problem. Here, logic gates control the reset operation via the IC1a–IC1b flip-flop, and the action is such that the reset command is given on the arrival of the $N$th clock pulse and is maintained while the clock pulse remains high, but is removed automati-

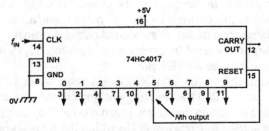

Figure 4.46   *Simple way of using the 74HC4017 as a divide-by-N (2 to 9) counter; circuit is shown set for divide-by-5 operation.*

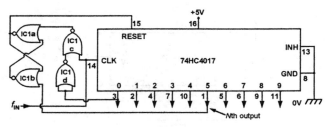

Figure 4.47   *Alternative divide-by-N circuit, set for divide-by-5 operation.*

matically when the clock pulse goes low again. Note in both diagrams that the circuit is shown set for divide-by-5 operation; also
note that the IC's carry out terminal is effectively disabled when $N$
values of less than 5 are used ('carry' signals can, however, easily be
derived from the decoded '0' or $N$ outputs).

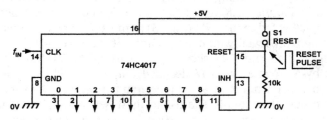

Figure 4.48   *74HC4017 set for sequence-and-stop operation.*

One of the 74HC4017's most important features is its provision of
ten fully decoded outputs, making the IC ideal for use in a whole
range of 'sequencing' operations in which the outputs are used to
drive LED displays, relays, sound generators, etc. *Figure 4.48* shows
how it can be connected to give 'sequence-and-stop' operation, in
which the IC stops clocking after completing a predetermined
counting sequence. In the diagram the counter is set to stop when its
INH terminal is driven high by the '9' output, but it can in fact be
inhibited via any one of the IC's decoded output terminals. The count
sequence can be restarted by pressing reset button S1, or by feeding
a positive pulse to the RESET pin.

If you want to use the 74HC4017 as a sequencing LED display
driver, you can use it in the 'moving dot' or 'chaser' mode (in which
only one LED is illuminated at any given moment) by using the basic
connections shown in *Figure 4.49*, in which the IC is shown used in
the divide-by-10 mode; note here that the LEDs share a common

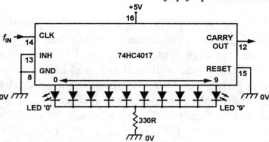

Figure 4.49 *Basic way of using the 74HC4017 as a moving-dot 10-LED 'chaser' circuit.*

current-limiting resistor, which with the value shown limits their ON currents to about 10mA.

If you have an application where you need to drive far more than ten LEDs in the sequential moving-dot mode, one option is to use two 74HC4017 ICs in the basic way shown in the 'multiplexed' circuit of *Figure 4.50*, which can sequentially step-drive as many as one hundred LEDs. Here, the divide-by-10 CARRY OUT signal of IC1 is fed to the CLK input of IC2, and the LEDs are connected in banks of ten with their anodes driven by IC1 and their cathodes taken to ground via switching transistors that are activated by the outputs of IC2. The circuit's basic action is such that, for any given LED to

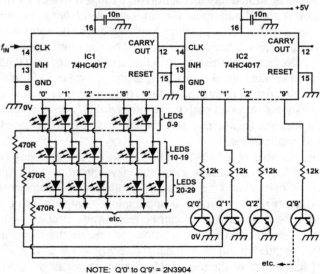

Figure 4.50 *Multiplexed moving-dot LED chaser circuit can drive up to 100 LEDs.*

be drived on, the appropriate outputs of both IC1 and IC2 must be high; LED12, for example, turns on only when outputs '2' of IC1 and '1' of IC2 are high, and so on. Thus, LEDs 0 to 9 are activated sequentially during clock pulses 0 to 9, and LEDs 10 to 19 are activated during pulses 10 to 19, and so on, right up to clock pulse 99, after which the whole sequence starts to repeat.

If desired, the circuit in *Figure 4.50* can be made to repeatedly sequence after a count of $N$ (rather than '99') by ANDing the appropriate outputs of IC1 and IC2 and feeding the ANDed signal directly to each IC's RESET (pin 15) terminal, which must have its ground connection removed. Thus, for an $N$ value of 27, outputs '2' of IC2 and '7' of IC1 must be ANDed, and the circuit needs only 27 LEDS and three switching transistors. Note that the 470R resistor connected in series with the collector of each transistor acts as a LED current limiter, and can be reduced to 220R if preferred.

## Synchronous or asynchronous counting?

In an asynchronous ripple counter, the output of one counting stage provides the clocking signal for the next stage, and as a result of each stage's progagation delay this action may cause unwanted glitches to appear on decoded outputs *as the counters switch between one set of states and another.* This glitching problem does not occur with synchronous counters, which are all clocked by the same input signal; in theory, therefore, it seems that synchronous counters are technically superior to asynchronous types. In practice, however, 'glitching' is a purely *transitory* occurrence, and the only time it is of real importance is when a decoded output is used to *directly* drive some sort of clocked logic network, and this situation occurs in relatively few practical applications.

Thus, in most real-world applications, the synchronous counter has no practical advantage over the asynchronous type, and the design engineer should – if he or she is sure that a synchronous type is not vital for use in a particular application – simply select the most cost-effective counter IC that can be used in the circuit in question. In most cases this will be a member of one of the asynchronous 74LS90 'decade' or 74LS93 'binary' (see *Figures 4.25* to *4.27*) families of ICs. Much of the rest of this chapter is in fact devoted to the former family, but before looking at this, note the following points about counter 'coding' systems.

## Counter 'coding' systems

A flip-flop counter has only two possible output states (either logic-0 or logic-1), and this number can be expressed as $2^N$, where $N$ is the number of flip-flop stages and in this case equals one. This simple formula holds true for any number of cascaded flip-flop counter stages; thus, if four stages are cascaded as shown in *Figure 4.51a*, in which the circuit's four outputs are notated A, B, C and D, the maximum possible number of different ABCD 'binary code' output states equals $2^4 = 16$. Note that this is the *maximum possible* number of output states, and is only obtained if the counters are wired in the ripple mode; if they are connected in the Johnson mode, only eight different possible output states are available.

Note in the circuit in *Figure 4.51a* that counter A changes state on the arrival of each new clock ($f_{IN}$) pulse, and that counter D changes state on the arrival of every eighth clock pulse. Consequentially, when the ABCD code is used to represent a 4-bit binary number (such as '1000') it is vital to remember that 'A' represents the Least Significant Bit (LSB) of that number, and 'D' represents its Most Significant Bit (MSB). In practice, a table of multi-bit binary codes

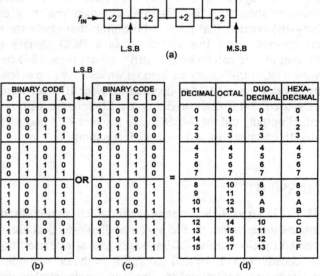

Figure 4.51 *A 4-bit binary code (a) can be represented as in (b) or (c), and can be translated into any of the code systems shown in (d).*

may be written with the LSB either on the right, as in the DCBA format shown in *Figure 4.51b*, or on the left, as in the ABCD format shown in *Figure 4.51c*; neither system has any real advantage over the other, so long as it is always remembered that 'A' represents the code's LSB. Similarly, when writing a binary code number such as '1110' in a report, etc., it is vital to make it clear to the reader whether this is an ABCD or a DCBA code, since '1110' may represent the 8th clock pulse in ABCD format or the 15th pulse in DCBA format, etc.

The tables of *Figures 4.51b* and *c* list all sixteen possible 4-bit binary codes, in both DCBA and ABCD format. Each of these codes can be used, via suitable decoding/activation circuitry, to represent or perform any action or thing that you care to think of (e.g., sound an alarm, unlatch a door, display the number '7'). In practice, however, they are usually used to represent numbers or letters in one or other of the four standard code systems listed in *Figure 4.51d*. Here, the decimal system has a base of ten, the octal has a base of eight, the duodecimal a base of twelve, and the hexadecimal (usually called 'hex') a base of sixteen.

The relevance of all this is that many popular counter ICs are internally configured to give outputs that comply with one or other of these code systems, and are supported by a variety of decoding/translating ICs. The 74LS90, for example, is a decade (divide-by-10) counter that has a 4-bit output that conforms to the standard decimal code; this is known as a BCD (binary coded decimal) output, and can be used to drive a 7-segment LED or LCD display via a BCD-to-7-segment decoder/driver IC, or up to ten independent devices via a BCD-to-decimal decoder IC, etc. Similarly, the rarely-used 74LS92 is a divide-by-12 counter with a 4-bit duodecimal output, and the 74LS93 (see *Figures 4.25* and *4.26*) is a divide-by-16 counter with a 4-bit hexadecimal output.

## The 74LS90 IC.

The 74LS90 is an asynchronous programmable counter/divider IC that contains independent divide-by-2 and divide-by-5 counters that are triggered by clock pulse falling-edges and can be used together to give decade (divide-by-10) counting with or without BCD outputs, or can be configured to give any whole-number division value from 2 to 9 inclusive. *Figure 4.52* shows the IC's functional

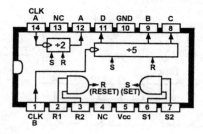

| R/S INPUTS | | | | OUTPUTS | | | | |
|---|---|---|---|---|---|---|---|---|
| R1 | R2 | S1 | S2 | D | C | B | A | |
| 1 | 1 | 0 | X | 0 | 0 | 0 | 0 | = BCD '0' |
| 1 | 1 | X | 0 | 0 | 0 | 0 | 0 | |
| X | X | 1 | 1 | 1 | 0 | 0 | 1 | = BCD '9' |
| 0 | X | 0 | X | | | | | |
| X | 0 | X | 0 | | | | COUNTING | |
| 0 | X | X | 0 | | | | | |
| X | 0 | 0 | X | | | | | |

X = DON'T CARE

Figure 4.52 *Functional diagram and R/S Truth Table of the 74LS90 decade counter IC with BCD outputs.*

diagram and its R/S (RESET/SET) Truth Table. Note that the two counters share SET and RESET lines that are controlled via 2-input AND gates; normally, each of these AND gates are disabled by tying at least one terminal low; the gates are active only when both inputs (R1-R2 for RESET, S1-S2 for SET) are driven high; when RESET is active, the DCBA outputs are driven to '0000' (= BCD '0'); when SET is active, the DCBA are driven to '1001' (= BCD '9'); the SET control has priority over RESET.

*Figures 4.53* and *4.54* show two very basic ways of using the 74LS90's counting ability. In *Figure 4.53* only the internal divide-by-2 counter is used; the divide-by-5 counter and SET/RESET gates are disabled, and the IC thus functions as a simple divide-by-2 (binary) counter. In *Figure 4.54* only the internal divide-by-5 counter

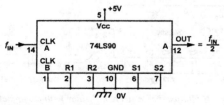

Figure 4.53 *The 74LS90 used as a divide-by-2 counter.*

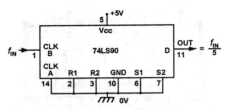

Figure 4.54  *The 74LS90 used as a divide-by-5 counter.*

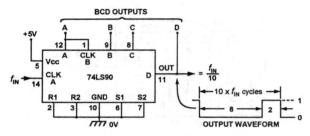

Figure 4.55  *The 74LS90 used as a decade counter/divider with BCD outputs.*

is used; the divide-by-2 counter and SET/RESET gates are disabled, and the IC thus acts as a simple divide-by-5 (quinary) counter.

*Figure 4.55* shows the IC used as a decade counter with BCD outputs. Here, both internal counters are used; $f_{IN}$ is fed to the input of the divide-by-2 counter, and the output (A) of this drives the input of the divide-by-5 counter; in this configuration the IC functions as a divide-by-10 counter with BCD outputs. Note that the final (pin 11) output waveform is asymmetrical, with a 1:4 Mark–Space ratio.

Figure 4.56 shows the IC used as a decade counter with a symmetrical (squarewave) output. Here, both internal counters are again used, but $f_{IN}$ is fed to the input of the divide-by-5 counter, and the output (D) of this drives the input of the divide-by-2 counter, which provides the final output; in this 'bi-quinary' configuration the IC

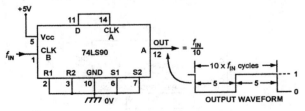

Figure 4.56  *The 74LS90 used as a decade divider with a symmetrical (squarewave) output waveform.*

| COUNT | OUTPUT | | |
|---|---|---|---|
| | D | C | B |
| 0 | 0 | 0 | 0 |
| 1 | 0 | 0 | 1 |
| 2 | 0 | 1 | 0 |
| 3 | 0 | 1 | 1 |
| 4 | 1 | 0 | 0 |

Figure 4.57 *Truth Table of the 74LS90's divide-by-5 (quinary) counter.*

thus functions as a divide-by-10 counter with a perfectly symmetrical (1:1 Mark–Space ratio) output. Note that the outputs of this circuit are not BCD coded.

The 74LS90 can be made to divide by any whole-number value from 2 to 9 inclusive by feeding appropriate outputs back to the IC's RESET or SET line so that the counter automatically resets each time the desired count number is reached. For divide values of 3, 4, 6 and 8 these feedback connections can be taken directly from the divide-by-5 counter's DCB outputs; *Figure 4.57* shows this counter's Truth Table. Thus, the IC can be configured as a divide-by-3 counter by using only its divide-by-5 counter, with RESET action provided via the B and C output so that it resets to '000' in the arrival of every count-3 pulse, and with the output taken from the C terminal as shown in *Figure 4.58a*. The IC can be made to give divide-by-6 action by using these same basic connections, but with the input

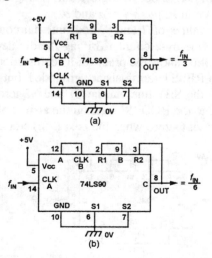

Figure 4.58 *The 74LS90 used as (a) a divide-by-3 or (b) divide-by-6 counter.*

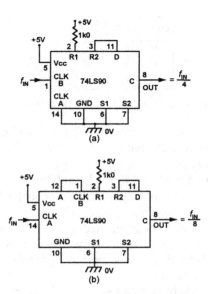

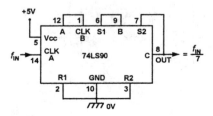

Figure 4.59   *The 74LS90 used as (a) a divide-by-4 or (b) divide-by-8 counter.*

applied via the divide-by-2 counter stage, as in *Figure 4.58 b*. These two circuits can be modified to give divide-by-4 or divide-by-8 action by tying the R1 input to logic-1 and taking the R2 input to output D, as shown in *Figures 4.59a and b*.

For divide-by values of 7 and 9, both internal counters must be used, with the divide-by-2 counter driving the divide-by-5 counter; Figures 4.60 and 4.61 show the practical IC connections. For divide-by-7 action, both RESET terminals are grounded, but outputs B and C are coupled to the SET line via the S1 and S2 terminals, so that both counters set to the BCD-'9' state on the arrival of the 6th clock pulse, and then reset to zero when the next (7th) clock pulse arrives.

Figure 4.60   *The 74LS90 used as a divide-by-7 counter.*

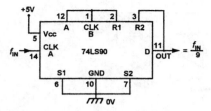

Figure 4.61 *The 74LS90 used as a divide-by-9 counter.*

For divide-by-9 action, the counters are RESET via the A and D outputs, which both go high on the 8 + 1 count.

## Greater-than-10 division

Even divide-by values greater than ten can usually be obtained by simply ripple-wiring suitably scaled standard counter stages, as shown in the examples of *Figure 4.62*. Thus, a divide-by-2 and a divide-by-6 stage give a ratio of 12, a divide-by-6 and a divide-by-6 give a ratio of 36, and so on. Of the examples shown, the divide-by-50 and divide-by-60 counters are of particular value in converting 50Hz or 60Hz power-line frequencies into 1-second timing signals with excellent long-term accuracy, and the multi-decade counters are of great value in generating precise decade-related signal frequencies from a single master oscillator.

*Figure 4.63* shows a practical example of a multi-decade frequency dividing circuit. Here, a crystal oscillator of the *Figure 3.45* type is used to generate a precision buffered-output 1MHz signal that is then divided down by six ripple-connected 74LS90 decade divider stages, to generate precision output frequencies of 1MHz, 100kHz,

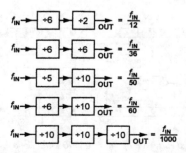

Figure 4.62 *Typical examples of division by numbers greater than ten.*

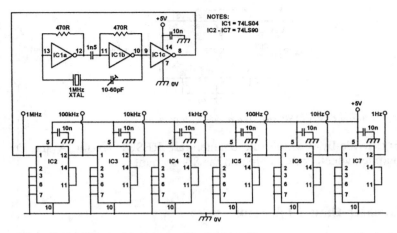

Figure 4.63   *TTL six-decade crystal frequency calibrator.*

10kHz, 1kHz, 100Hz, 10Hz and 1Hz, which can be used as frequency or timing calibration standards, etc. Note that each 74LS90 ICs is connected in the *Figure 4.56* decade divider mode and generates a symmetrical squarewave output that is very rich in odd harmonic frequencies, e.g. the 10kHz output also generates strong 30kHz, 50kHz, 70kHz, etc., output signals.

## The 74LS390 IC

The 74LS390 (and its CMOS counterpart, the 74HC390) is a dual decade divider IC that can be regarded as a Dual version of the basic 74LS90, but with no SET control and with greatly simplified RESET

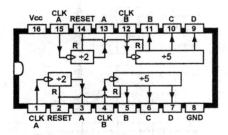

Figure 4.64   *Functional diagram of the 74LS390 Dual decade (Bi-quinary) counter IC.*

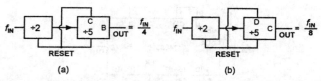

Figure 4.65 *Basic ways of using a 74LS390 decade divider section to give (a) divide-by-4 or (b) divide-by-8 action.*

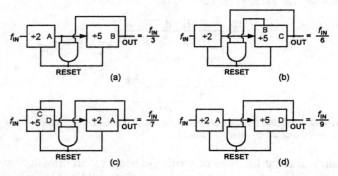

Figure 4.66 *Ways of using the 74LS390's decade dividers and an external 2-input AND gate to give divide-by values of (a) 3, (b) 6, (c) 7, or (d) 9.*

| DIVIDE-BY VALUE | BASIC CIRCUIT |
|---|---|
| 2 | IN — $\div2$ — OUT |
| 4 | IN — $\div2$ ► $\div2$ — OUT |
| 5 | IN — $\div5$ — OUT |
| 10 (BCD OUTPUTS) | IN — $\div2$ ► $\div5$ — OUT  A B C D  BCD OUTPUTS |
| 10 (SYMMETRICAL OUTPUT) | IN — $\div5$ ► $\div2$ — OUT |
| 20 | IN — $\div2$ ► $\div10$ — OUT |
| 25 | IN — $\div5$ ► $\div5$ — OUT |
| 50 | IN — $\div5$ ► $\div10$ — OUT |
| 100 | IN — $\div10$ ► $\div10$ — OUT |

Figure 4.67 *Basic ways of using the 74LS390 to give various 'divide-by' values.*

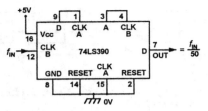

Figure 4.68   *The 74LS390 used as a divide-by-50 counter.*

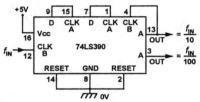

Figure 4.69   *The 74LS390 used as a divide-by-100 counter with symmetrical divide-by-10 and divide-by-100 outputs.*

circuitry. It is (at the time of writing) cheaper than the 74LS90, and is thus a very attractive alternative to the 74LS90 in most applications where a SET facility is not needed. *Figure 4.64* shows the functional diagram of the 74LS390; each 'decade' counter is a bi-quinary type and consists of divide-by-2 and divide-by-5 counters that can be used independently but share a common RESET facility (RESET is normally grounded, and resets the decade counter to the '0000' BCDA state when taken to logic-1); the divide-by-5 counter has the same Truth Table as that used in the 74LS90 (see *Figure 4.57*).

Note in *Figure 4.64* that one decade counter appears in the lower part of the diagram, between the 'lower' (1 to 7) set of pin numbers, and the other is in the upper part, between the 'upper' (9 to 15) pin numbers; for convenience, these counters are therefore referred to in the following text by terms such as 'upper-2', 'lower-5', 'upper-10', etc.

The 74LS390 is a very easy IC to use. In each decade, the '2' and '5' counters can be used in any combination, making divide-by values of 2, 5 and 10 directly available (unwanted counters are disabled by simply grounding their CLK terminals), and each decade counter can be configured to give either a BCD or a symmetrical output. If desired, each 'decade' counter can alternatively be configured to give counts of 4 or 8 by connecting its RESET terminal to the C or D outputs as shown in *Figure 4.65*, or can be made to give counts of 3, 6, 7 or 9 by feeding various outputs back to the RESET terminal via an external 2-input AND gate as shown in *Figure 4.66*. A very large total number of divide-by combinations are thus available from the 74LS390 IC; *Figure 4.67* shows how values of 2, 4, 5, 10, 20, 25, 50, and 100 can be obtained by just ripple-wiring the IC's standard '2' and '5' counters. It would be tedious to draw up a full set of wiring diagrams for all of these divide-by combinations, but *Figure 4.68* shows how a divide-by-50 counter can be made by ripple-wiring the upper-5, lower-2 and lower-5 counters and disabling upper-2, and *Figure 4.69* shows a divide-by-100 counter with symmetrical outputs made by ripple-wiring the upper-5, upper-2, lower-5, and lower-2 counters. In practice this versatile IC can, by using ANDed RESET control where necessary, be configured to give any desired whole-number divide-by value in the range 2 to 100 inclusive.

# 5 Special counter/dividers

All of the clocked flip-flop counters described in Chapter 4 are standard 'up-counting' types: each of them starts its count with all binary outputs set to the '0' state, and the outputs then increment upwards on successive clock pulses until the maximum count is reached, and the whole counting process then restarts on the arrival of the next pulse. These up-counters are excellent for use in most practical counting applications, but there are some occasions when more specialized types of counter are needed; this chapter describes some of the special counter/divider ICs that are available, including 'presettable' and 'down' and 'up/down' counting types.

## Back to basics

Chapter 4 explained how D-type and JK flip-flops work and described how a D-type can be made to act as a binary divider (divide-by-2) stage by connecting its D and NOT-Q terminals together as shown in *Figure 5.1a*, and a JK-type can be made to act in the same way by tying its J and K terminals to logic-1 as shown in

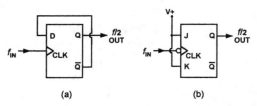

(a)               (b)

Figure 5.1 *General circuit diagram of (a) D-type and (b) JK divide-by-2 stages; the D-type uses rising-edge triggering; the JK is falling-edge triggered.*

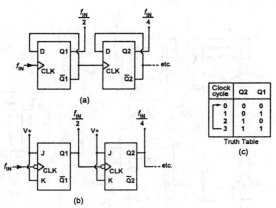

(a)

(b)

| Clock cycle | Q2 | Q1 |
|---|---|---|
| 0 | 0 | 0 |
| 1 | 0 | 1 |
| 2 | 1 | 0 |
| 3 | 1 | 1 |

Truth Table

(c)

Figure 5.2  *Basic ways of using (a) D-type and (b) JK stages in 'up-counting' ripple modes; (c) Truth Table for both circuits.*

*Figure 5.1b.* Note from the symbols of these diagrams that the D-type's actions are triggered by the rising-edges of the clock signals, and the JK's are triggered by falling-edges.

*Figure 5.2* shows how D-type or JK divider stages can be cascaded to make ripple-mode binary counters in which the output of the first stage is used to clock the input of the second stage, and so on for however many stages there are. In rising-edge triggered D-type circuits the clock pulses are taken from NOT-Q outputs, as shown in *Figure 5.2a*, but in falling-edge triggered JK circuits they are taken from Q outputs, as in *Figures 5.2b*. Both circuits have the same Q-output Truth Table, which for a 2-stage ripple counter is as shown in *Figure 5.2c*; if you compare this Table with that of *Figure 4.51* (in Chapter 4) you will notice that the 4-step sequential binary coded outputs of *Figure 5.2* correspond with normal decimal (BCD) coding, and run 0-1-2-3-0-etc. as the clock goes through cycles 0-1-2-3-0-etc.

Thus, the *Figure 5.2* type of counter gives a sequentially upwards-counting clocking cycle, which repeatedly runs from 0 to 3 in a 2-bit counter, or 0 to 7 in a 3-bit counter, and so on. Consequently, all circuits of this basic type are known as 'up' counters, irrespective of their bit-count or whether they give a synchronous or asynchronous type of clocking action, etc.

The counting action of a ripple counter can be reversed, so that it counts 'downwards' rather than 'upwards' by using the basic connections shown in *Figure 5.3*, in which the clocking output of

## 152  Modern TTL Circuits

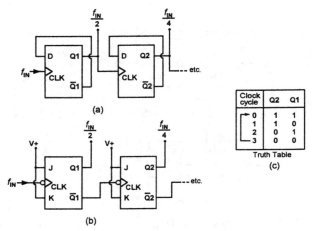

(a)

(b)

| Clock cycle | Q2 | Q1 |
|---|---|---|
| 0 | 1 | 1 |
| 1 | 1 | 0 |
| 2 | 0 | 1 |
| 3 | 0 | 0 |

Truth Table

(c)

Figure 5.3   Basic ways of using (a) D-type and (b) JK stages in 'down-counting' ripple modes; (c) Truth Table for both circuits.

each stage is taken from the complement of that used in *Figure 5.2* (i.e. from Q rather than NOT-Q, or *vice versa*). A 2-bit counter of this type generates the Truth Table shown in *Figure 5.3c*, in which the sequential BCD coding runs 3-2-1-0-3-etc. as the clock goes through cycles 0-1-2-3-0-etc. This type of counter gives a sequentially downwards-counting clocking cycle, which repeatedly runs from 3 to 0 in a 2-bit counter, or 7 to 0 in a 3-bit counter, and so on. Consequently, all circuits of this basic type are known as 'down' counters, irrespective of their bit-count or whether they give a synchronous or asynchronous type of clocking action, etc.

A ripple counter can be configured to count in either direction by fitting it with gate-controlled clock-source options, as shown in the

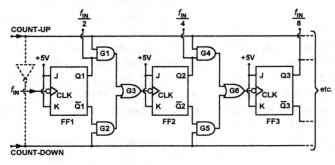

Figure 5.4   Basic JK-type UP/DOWN counter.

JK example of *Figure 5.4*. Here, when the COUNT-UP line is biased to logic-1 and the COUNT-DOWN line is biased to logic-0 the G1 and G4 AND gates are enabled and pass 'Q' clock signals to FF2 and FF3 (etc.), but gates G2 and G5 are disabled and block the NOT-Q signals; the circuit thus acts like that of *Figure 5.2b* under this condition, and gives an 'up' counting action. But when the COUNT-DOWN line is biased to logic-1 and COUNT-UP is at logic-0 the G1 and G4 gates are disabled and G2 and G5 are enabled and pass NOT-Q clock signals, and under this condition the circuit acts like that of *Figure 5.3b* and gives a 'down' counting action. All circuits of this basic type are known as 'up/down' counters, irrespective of their bit-count or their precise form of construction, etc.

Note that the UP/DOWN circuit in *Figure 5.4* uses individual COUNT-UP and COUNT-DOWN control lines, which must always be connected in opposite logic states. The circuit can be modified for control via a single UP/DOWN input terminal by wiring an inverter between the two lines, as shown dotted in the diagram, so that the circuit gives UP counting when the upper line is biased to logic-1, and DOWN counting when it is biased to logic-0. Some UP/DOWN counters use two clock lines, one for UP counting and the other for DOWN counting; these counters are internally similar to *Figure 5.4* but have the clock and direction-control lines effectively combined via logic networks that control the clock feed to FF1 as well as all the other flip-flop stages.

Thus, the electronics engineer has many options when designing modern counter/divider circuits. The usual option is to use a conventional synchronous or asynchronous up-counting IC, and most of the finer points of this subject are covered in Chapter 4. There are also the options of using DOWN or UP/DOWN counters; both of these options are dealt with later in the present chapter, but first it is necessary to look at yet another option, that of using 'programmable' counter/divider ICs.

## 'Programmable' counters

Most 4-bit 'counter' ICs are designed for use in both counting and dividing applications, and are thus known as counter/divider ICs. *Figure 5.5*, for example, shows how two ordinary BCD decade counter stages (such as those from the 74LS390 Dual decade counter) can be used as a divide-by-100 circuit that gives a stable

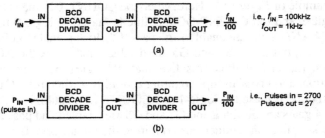

(a)

(b)

Figure 5.5   *Two decade 'dividers' used to give (a) frequency division or (b) pulse-count division.*

output frequency of 1kHz if fed with a stable 100kHz clock signal (*Figure 5.5a*), or produces 27 output pulses (cycles) when clocked via 2700 randomly-timed input pulses (*Figure 5.5b*). Note that neither of these circuits gives any visual output information (via 7-segment displays, etc).

*Figure 5.6* shows, in block diagram form, how the *Figure 5.5b* pulse cycle divider circuit can be converted into a pulse *counter* by simply fitting it with digital readout circuitry, so that the user can actually see the results of the divide-by-100 action. Thus the basic difference between a counter and a divider is one of usage; a counter usually has a visual readout, and a divider has not.

All conventional 'up' counters are provided with a RESET facility that enables their 'Q' outputs to be set to zero at any time, thus giving a BCD '0' output. This facility is – as described in Chapter 4 – also useful in enabling the counter's 'divide-by' figure

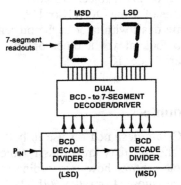

Figure 5.6   *The pulse-count divider of Figure 5.5(b) can be used as a pulse counter by fitting it with a digital readout facility.*

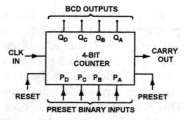

BCD OUTPUTS

Figure 5.7 *The 'Q' outputs of a PROGRAMMABLE counter can be forced into preset binary states via a PRESET control.*

to be preset to any desired value, *N*, by connecting the outputs back to the RESET terminal so that the outputs reset to the BCD '0' state on the arrival of every *N*th clock pulse, but a weakness here is that the IC has to be hard-wired to give a specific divide-by figure, and this sometimes involves the use of external gating circuitry, etc. One way around this snag is to provide the IC with an additional PROGRAMMING control that enables its outputs to be set to any desired binary values when the control is activated.

*Figure 5.7* illustrates the basic idea behind the programmable counter. Here, any desired 4-bit binary code can be applied to the IC's four 'P' terminals, and the IC's 4-bit output is forced to agree with this code whenever the PRESET control is activated. In practice, this type of IC may be known as a 'programmable' or 'presettable' counter, its input facilities may be named PRESET or PARALLEL LOAD or JAM controls, and the controls may be activated by a logic-0 or logic-1 input or by rising or falling clock edges, etc., depending on the individual device and its manufacturer. In all cases, however, these devices operate in the basic way described above.

*Figure 5.8* shows one basic way of using the PRESET control to make a divider with any desired whole-number 'divide-by' value from 2 to 9. Assume here that the PRESET terminal is active-high and is shorted to the CARRY output as shown; this output goes high

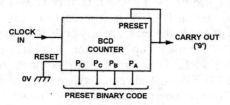

Figure 5.8 *Basic way of using the PRESET facility of a programmable divider.*

on the arrival of each decimal-9 clock pulse and thus sets the IC's 'Q' outputs to the preset state under this condition. Thus, if the DCBA preset inputs are set to '0000' the IC will go though a 0-1-2-3-4-5-6-7-8-0-etc. counting cycle and thus give a divide-by-9 action, but if they are preset to '0010' (decimal-2) the IC will go through a 2-3-4-5-6-7-8-2-etc. counting cycle and thus give a divide-by-7 action, and so on. This type of divider thus goes through X-to-8 counting cycles, where X is the number set on the DCBA preset inputs; note that this action is useful in a divider, but of little value in a decade counter (in which counting usually starts from zero).

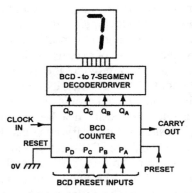

Figure 5.9  *Basic way of using the PRESET facility of a programmable counter.*

*Figure 5.9* shows one basic way of using the PRESET function in a counter. Here, the 7-segment readout displays the current preset BCD number while the PRESET control is activated, and the counter then counts up from that number when the PRESET contol is deactivated; the BCD inputs may be derived from special switches, or may be taken from the BCD outputs of a slowly clocked up/down counter, etc. This latter technique is of special value in time-setting electronic clocks, for example.

Yet another use of the PRESET facility is as a master RESET control if the normal RESET is in permanent use as a divide-by controller; in this case the preset binary code is simply set to '0000'.

Several 74LS-series 'up' counter ICs are provided with 'programmable' PRESET facilities. Amongst them are the 74LS160, 74LS162 and 74LS196 decade counters, and the 74LS161, 74LS163 and 74LS197 4-bit binary counters. Most 'down' and 'up/down' counter/divider ICs are provided with 'programming' facilities.

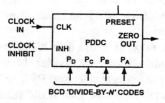

Figure 5.10 *Basic features of a programmable decade 'down' counter (PDDC).*

## 'Down' counters

'Down' counters are very specialized devices and *ideally* should have the basic facilities illustrated in *Figure 5.10*. Namely, they must be programmable (presettable) and have a special output that activates when the 'zero' count is reached, plus an input that inhibits the clocking action when activated. In the diagram, PRESET and INH (clock inhibit) are assumed to be active-high, and the ZERO OUT terminal goes high only when ZERO count is reached. In the following text and diagrams only decade (rather than binary) versions of these devices are considered, and the abbreviation 'PDDC' is used to indicate a programmable decade down counter.

A PDDC can be used as a simple decade divider by connecting it as shown in *Figure 5.11*, with its PRESET and INH controls, etc., grounded, so that the counter repeatedly cycles through its basic

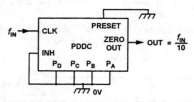

Figure 5.11 *PDDC connected as a simple decade frequency divider.*

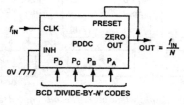

Figure 5.12 *PDDC connected as a programmable frequency divider.*

BCD count, from 9 to 0 and then back to 9 again, and so on. The output, taken from the ZERO OUT terminal, goes high for one full clock cycle in every ten.

*Figure 5.12* shows how to use a PDDC in its most important mode, as a programmable frequency divider. Here, the divide-by-*N* code is applied to the preset terminals and PRESET is controlled by the ZERO OUT terminal. Suppose that at the start of the count the BCD number 4 has been preset into the counter. On the arrival of the first clock pulse the counter decrements to 3, on the second pulse to 2, on the third to 1, and on the fourth to 0, at which point the ZERO OUT terminal goes high and presets the BCD number 4 back into the counter, so the whole sequence starts over again and ZERO OUT goes back low. Thus, the PDDC repeatedly counts by the number (4) set on the preset inputs, and the output (from the ZERO OUT terminal) takes the form of a narrow pulse with a width of a few tens of nanoseconds.

Note that the really important thing about the circuit in *Figure 5.12* circuit is that it automatically divides by whatever BCD number is set on the preset terminals (compare this action with that of the programmable 'up' counter of *Figure 5.8*, in which the preset BCD number is related in a complex way to the divide-by number). This feature is of special importance in what are known as 'decade

Figure 5.13   *When conventional counters are cascaded they give a final output equal to the product of the individual division values.*

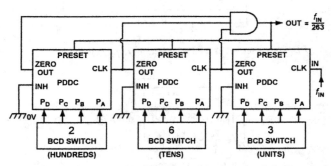

Figure 5.14   *When PDDCs are wired in the 'decade cascaded v.' mode they give a final 'divide-by' value equal to the SUM of their individual DECADE values.*

cascadable' counter/divider applications, in which the overall division values are easily and directly programmable; *Figures 5.13* and *5.14* illustrate the salient points of the subject.

*Figure 5.13* shows a basic circuit in which three conventional counters, with 'divide-by' values of 2, 6 and 3, are directly cascaded, to give an overall division value of 36, i.e. equal to the *product* of the individual divide-by values. *Figure 5.14*, on the other hand, shows what happens when PDDCs with divide-by values of (reading from left to right) 2, 6 and 3 are wired in the 'decade cascadable' mode; in this case the overall divide-by value is equal to the *sum* of the individual *decade* values, and (since the decades are graded in 'hundreds', 'tens', and 'units') equals 263, or whatever other 3-digit number is set up on the PRESET switches. The circuit operates as follows.

Note in *Figure 5.14* that the ZERO OUT signals of the three PDDCs are fed to a 3-input AND gate that drives the PRESET (and OUT) line, and the PRESET line thus becomes active only when all three ZERO OUT signals coincide. With this point in mind, assume that at the start of the count cycle the BCD number 263 is loaded into the counters as shown. For the first few counts in the cycle the 'units' PDDC counts from 3 down to 0 and then goes into the normal '9-to-0' decade down-counting mode, passing a clock pulse on to the 'tens' PDDC each time the '0' state is reached. Thus, the 'tens' PDDC receives its first clock pulse after three input cycles and counts down from 6 to 5, but from then on is clocked down one step for every ten input cycles, until its own count falls to zero, at which point it passes a clock pulse on to the 'hundreds' counter and simultaneously goes into the decade down-counting mode. One hundred input cycles later the 'hundreds' PDDC receives another clock pulse and its own count falls to zero; one hundred input cycles after that (on the 263rd count of the cycle) it receives a third clock pulse, and at that instant the ZERO OUT signals of all three PDDCs are active, so the AND gate activates the PRESET line and loads the BCD number 263 back into the counters, and the whole sequence starts over again.

Thus, the circuit in *Figure 5.14* repeatedly divides by 263 or whatever other three-decade number is programmed in, and produces a narrow output pulse (from the AND gate) on completion of each 'divide-by-263' counting cycle. This output pulse is only a few tens of nanoseconds wide (the width is dictated by the circuit's propagation delays), but is wide enough to trigger digital elements such as counters or monostables, etc.

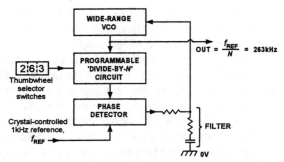

Figure 5.15   *A programmable divide-by-N circuit can be used in conjunction with a PLL to make a precision programmable frequency synthesiser.*

## PDDC applications

'Decade cascaded' PDDC circuits of the type shown in *Figure 5.14* have important practical application in frequency synthesis, programmable counting and programmable timing. In frequency synthesis the PDDCs are wired as a programmable frequency divider and used in conjunction with a phase-locked loop (PLL) as shown in *Figure 5.15*. Here, the output of a wide-range voltage-controlled oscillator (VCO) is fed, via the programmable divide-by-$N$ counter, to one input of a phase detector, which has its other input taken from a crystal-controlled reference-frequency generator. The phase detector produces an output voltage proportional to the difference between the two input frequencies; this voltage is filtered and fed back to the VCO control in such a way that the VCO automatically self-adjusts to bring the variable input frequency of the phase detector to the same value as the reference frequency, at which point the PLL is said to be 'locked'.

Note that, when the PLL is locked, the VCO's output frequency is $N$ times that on the variable input of the phase detector, and is thus $N$ times that of the reference generator, e.g. if $N = 263$ and $f_{REF} =$

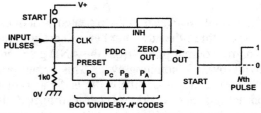

Figure 5.16   *PDDC used as a programmable 'down' counter.*

1kHz, $f_{OUT}$ = 263kHz, and has crystal precision. Thus, this circuit can be used to generate precise output frequencies that are variable in 1kHz steps via the three-decade thumbwheel selector switches.

*Figure 5.16* shows, in basic form, how a single PDDC can be used as a 1-to-9 counting circuit. Here, the INH terminal is connected directly to ZERO OUT, so that the PDDC's clocking action is inhibited when the PDDC is in the '0' counting state; normally, the circuit is locked into this state, with its output at the logic-1 level. Suppose now that the BCD number 6 is preset via the START button; the output immediately switches low, and on the arrival of each clock pulse the PDDC counts down one step until finally, on the arrival of the sixth pulse, the ZERO OUT terminal goes high again and activates INH, causing any further pulses to be ignored. The count sequence is then complete, but can be restarted via the START button.

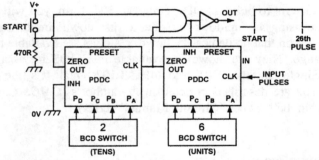

Figure 5.17 *Two-decade programmable 'down' counter, set for count-26 operation.*

*Figure 5.17* shows how the basic circuit can be turned into a useful two-decade unit that can be programmed to count by any number up to 99 and has an output that goes high for the full duration of the counting cycle. This type of circuit is useful in (for example) controlling automatic packing machines in applications where $N$ objects have to be loaded into each container, but the $N$ value is often varied. In such an application, the object feeder must generate a clock pulse each time it feeds an object into the container, and must be so arranged that it directs its feed to the next container when the first one is registered 'full'.

Finally, *Figure 5.18* shows, in basic form, how the simple circuit of *Figure 5.16* can be made to act as a programmable timer with an

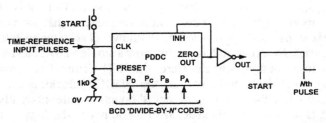

Figure 5.18  *PDDC connected as a programmable timer.*

output that goes high as the START button is pressed but then goes low again a preset time later. Here, the clock signal (which ideally should be synchronized with the START signal) is taken from a time-reference source (e.g. 1 pulse per second or minute). This basic circuit can be expanded to two decades by using connections similar to those of *Figure 5.17*.

If you want to build a PDDC circuit in TTL form, you will have to do so using an 'up/down' counter in its 'down' mode, for the simple reason that no dedicated 'down' counters are available in the TTL range. They are, however, available in CMOS forms as the 4522 'Single' and the 40102 and 74HC40102 'Dual' ICs (the 4522 and 40102 are described in detail in the author's *CMOS Circuits Manual* in the Newnes 'Circuits Manual' series).

## 'Up/down' counters

'Up/down' counters are the most versatile of all counter types. They are invariably programmable and synchronous in operation, are available in both BCD decade and 4-bit binary counting forms, and in most cases have the basic facilities shown in *Figure 5.19*, i.e., they have PRESET inputs and a full set of 'Q' outputs, can be set to clock

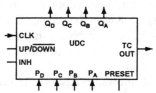

Figure 5.19  *Basic features of a conventional UP/DOWN counter (UDC).*

'up' or 'down' via a single UP/DOWN terminal, have a clock inhibit (INH) facility, and have a 'TC OUT' output that becomes active when the counter reaches its Terminal Count ('0' in down-counting mode, '9' in decade up-counting mode, etc). The 74LS192 (BCD decade) and 74LS193 (4-bit binary) up/down counters differ from this norm in that they use separate 'up' and 'down' clocks and have no master INH facility, but are otherwise similar. Individual IC types differ mainly in their pin terminology (the INH terminal may, for example, be named NOT ENABLE or CARRY IN) and in their details of use, e.g. INH or TC OUT may be active-high on one IC type and active-low on another.

Because of their versatility and consequent high sales volumes, up/down counters are often available at lower cost than more conventional types, and can thus be used instead of normal or programmable 'up' or 'down' counters in a wide range of applications, as well as being invaluable in many add/subtract and up/down differential counting applications, etc. *Figures 5.20* to *5.30* show a selection of different ways of using the basic up/down counter of *Figure 5.19*; in these diagrams it is assumed that the INH, PRESET and TC OUT controls are active-high, and that the IC counts 'up' when the UP/DOWN control is biased high, and 'down' when it is biased low.

*Figure 5.20* shows a decade up/down counter used as a simple decade 'up' counter/divider; note that PRESET can be used as a RESET control that forces the outputs into the '0000' state when it is taken high. *Figure 5.21* shows the up/down counter used as a programmable 'up' divider of the *Figure 5.8* type, and *Figure 5.22* shows it wired as a programmable frequency divider of the far more useful *Figure 5.12* down-counting PDDC type, in which the divide-by value equals the BCD value set on the programming terminals;

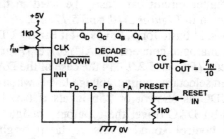

Figure 5.20 *A decade UDC used as a simple decade 'up'-counter/divider.*

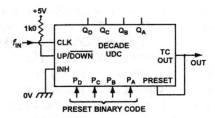

Figure 5.21 *A decade UDC used as a programmable 'up'-divider.*

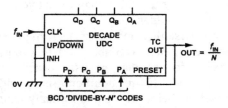

Figure 5.22 *A decade UDC used as a 'down' (PDDC) programmable frequency divider.*

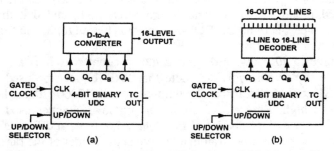

Figure 5.23 *Basic ways of using a Binary UDC as (a) a DAC driver or (b) a multi-line selector.*

this basic down-counter circuit can easily be used in the decade cascaded modes shown in *Figures 5.14* and *5.17*, etc.

*Figure 5.23* shows, in basic form, how a 4-bit Binary UDC can be used as a digital-to-analogue converter (DAC) driver *(Figure 5.23a)* or a multi-line selector *(Figure 5.23b)*. In the case of the DAC driver, this produces sixteen selectable output voltage levels when driven by the 4-bit Binary UDC as shown, or 256 levels if two UDCs are cascaded to give 8-bit DAC drive; these output voltage levels can easily be used to control sound levels or lamp brightness for example, via suitable adaptor circuitry. The circuit in *Figure 5.23b*

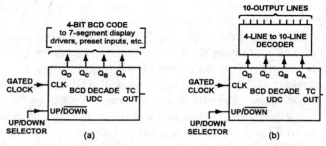

Figure 5.24 *Basic ways of using a BCD decade UDC as (a) a 4-bit BCD code generator or (b) a multi-line selector.*

can be used as a multi-line selector, in which only one of the sixteen output lines is active (usually active-low) at any one time, by using the UDC to drive a 4-line to 16-line decoder as shown, or can be used like a single-pole 16-way switch by using it to drive a CMOS analogue switch IC such as the 4067B, etc.

*Figure 5.24* shows, in basic form, how a BCD decade UDC can be used as a 4-bit BCD code generator *(Figure 5.24a)* or a multi-line selector *(Figure 5.24b)* . In the case of the BCD code generator, note that the BCD code can be used to drive PRESET inputs and/or 7-segment digital displays, etc., and is thus useful in the time-setting of clocks and presetting of counters or dividers, for example. The circuit in *Figure 5.24b* can be used in the same ways as the multi-line selector of *Figure 5.23*, but gives only ten outputs; note, however, that its BCD output can be used to simultaneously drive a digital display that shows the prevailing output number, and that by using multiplexing or ANDing techniques two of these basic circuits can be cascaded to make up to one hundred individual outputs available.

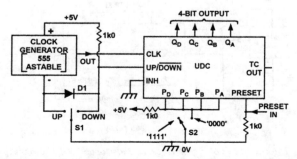

Figure 5.25 *Typical connections of a gate-clocked free-ranging UDC circuit.*

*Figure 5.25* shows typical connections that may be used in practical versions of the *Figure 5.23* or *5.24* gate-clocked circuits. Here, a 555 IC is used in the astable mode as a clock-waveform generator, and is normally disabled but can be gated on by grounding its negative supply line via centre-biased toggle switch S1, which also controls the UDC's up/down direction. The UDC's preset inputs are shown configured so that they give codes of '0000' (= BCD '0') when S2 is closed or '1111' (= terminal count in binary up-counting mode) when S2 is open, enabling a binary UDC to be instantly set to either end of its counting range.

Note that the circuit in *Figure 5.25* gives a 'free-ranging' clocking action, i.e. when it reaches the terminal count in a clocking cycle it automatically jumps back to the 'start' count in the arrival of the next clock pulse. A popular alternative to this is an 'end-stopped' counting action, in which counting automatically ceases when the terminal count is reached, and can only be restored by reversing the count direction, i.e. so that a lower number can only be reached by clocking down, and a higher number can only be reached by clocking up. If the UDC's INH and TC OUT terminals have the same active states (both active-high or active-low) this action can be obtained by simply shorting these two terminals together as shown in *Figure 5.26*, but if they have opposite active states an inverter stage must be wired between TC OUT and INH as indicated in the diagram (the UDC's 'preset' connections are not shown in the diagram).

Note that the free-ranging circuit in *Figure 5.25* can be expanded to give an 8-bit output by cascading it with another UDC, with both INH terminals grounded and with both UP/DOWN terminals shorted together, etc., and with the TC OUT of the first UDC providing the

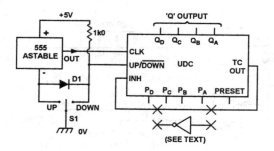

Figure 5.26  *Typical circuit of a gate-clocked 'end-stopped' UDC circuit (preset connections not shown).*

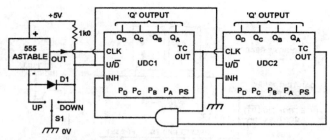

Figure 5.27  *Basic method of expanding the 'end-stopped' UDC circuit of Figure 5.26 to give an 8-Bit output.*

CLK signal of the second IC. The procedure for expanding the end-stopped version is a little more complex.

*Figure 5.27* shows how to expand the circuit in *Figure 5.25* so that it gives 8-bit end-stopped clocking operation. In this case both UP/DOWN terminals are again shorted together, and the TC OUT of UDC1 provides the CLK signal for UDC2, but the TC OUTs of both counters are ANDed and fed to INH of UDC1, thus providing bidirectional end-stopping, and INH of UDC2 is grounded. Note in these expanded circuits that the first UDC (UDC1) provides the four least-significant bits of the 8-bit output.

## 'Add/subtract' circuits

A UDC can be made to perform add/subtract actions by simply switching it to the 'up' mode for addition or the 'down' mode for subtraction and clocking-in one input pulse per add or subtract unit. This type of action is useful in applications such as car-park monitoring, for example, and *Figure 5.28* shows the basic circuit of a monitor that keeps track of the number of cars in a car-park with a maximum capacity of 99 vehicles. Assume here that the car-park's entry/exit is fitted with a system that generates a single clock pulse and a logic-1 level whenever a vehicle enters the site, and a single pulse and a logic-0 level whenever a vehicle leaves the site, and is fitted with foolproof logic circuitry that ensures that only one of these sets of states can occur at any given moment. Also assume that the circuit uses two UDCs connected in the end-stopped counting fashion shown in *Figure 5.27*, and thus cannot count below zero or above 99; the basic circuit operates as follows.

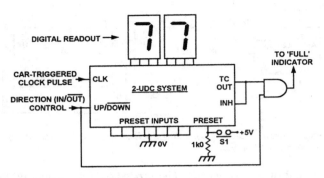

Figure 5.28   *Simple car-park 'number-of-cars-parked' indicator (99 maximum).*

At the start of each working day, the car-park attendant operates PRESET switch S1 and thus sets the digital readouts to zero. The readout then increments by one count each time a vehicle enters the car-park or decrements by one count each time a vehicle leaves, thus giving a running count of the number of vehicles parked; when the total number of 'parked' vehicles reaches 99, the TC OUT and UP/$\overline{\text{DOWN}}$ terminals are both at logic-1 and are ANDed and used to activate the car park's 'FULL' sign (note that this AND gate stops the 'FULL' sign activating when TC OUT goes high at zero-count in the 'down' mode).

The basic circuit in *Figure 5.28* has two obvious defects. First, it has no facility for correcting counting errors, such as occur if the attendant activates the PRESET switch without realizing that a number of vehicles remained locked-in overnight. Second, it only activates the 'FULL' sign correctly if the car-park has a maximum capacity of 99 vehicles. *Figure 5.29* shows how both of these defects can be overcome. Here, S2 is a biased 2-pole toggle switch that is normally set to AUTO; any start-of-the-day counting errors can be rectified – after setting the count to zero via S1 – by moving S2 to the MANUAL position and feeding-in manually-triggered clock UP pulses via S3 until the reading is correct. The second defect is overcome by a set of gates connected as a MAXIMUM-COUNT DETECTOR, which gives a logic-1 output and activates the 'FULL' sign only when the system's two 4-bit BCD output codes correspond with the car park's maximum capacity.

An alternative – and probably better – approach to the 'car park' problem is to have a system that displays the available number of

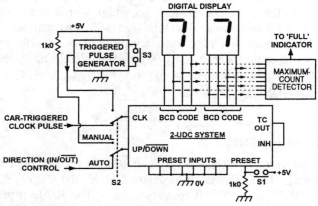

Figure 5.29 *Improved car-park 'number-of-cars-parked' indicator can show any 'FULL' value up to 99 maximum.*

parking spaces, rather than the number of parked cars. *Figure 5.30* shows a basic circuit of this type. Here, the car-park's entry/exit system is made to generate a low (down-count) level when a car enters, and a high (up-count) level when a car leaves. When the S1 PRESET switch is operated it loads the car park's BCD 'maximum number of spaces' code into the system, and this number appears on the display; any real-life errors in this 'spaces' reading can be corrected by setting S2 to MANUAL and operating S3. The 'spaces' readout then decrements by one count each time a car enters the car-park or increments by one count each time a car leaves, thus giving

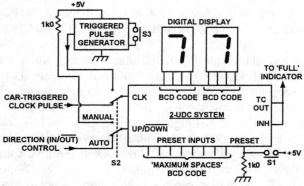

Figure 5.30 *Car-park 'spaces-available' indicator can show up to 98-maximum spaces.*

a running count of the number of available spaces; when this number falls to zero the TC OUT terminal goes high and activates the car park's 'FULL' sign (note that this sign will also activate if the 'spaces' count *rises* to 99, so this circuit functions correctly up to a maximum 'spaces' value of only 98, unless suitably modified; the maximum capacity can easily be expanded to 998 spaces, by basing the design on 3-UDC system).

### 'Up/down' counter ICs.

Several different 'UP/DOWN' counter ICs are readily available in CMOS and TTL IC forms. In ordinary CMOS, the 4029B, 4510B, 4516B, 40192B and 40193B are very popular. The 4029B is unusual in that it has a control terminal that enables it to count in either decade or binary mode; the 4510B decade and 4516B binary counters are single-clock ICs with identical pin notations, and the 40192B decade and 40193B binary counters are dual-clock ICs with identical pin notations (details of these five ICs are given in the author's *CMOS Circuits Manual* in the Newnes 'Circuits Manual' series of books); four of these five CMOS ICs are also available in the 74HC series as the 74HC4510, 74HC4516, 74HC40192 and 74HC40193.

In the 74LS TTL series, the most popular 'UP/DOWN' counters are the 74LS190 and 74LS192 'decade' types and the 74LS191 and 74LS193 'binary' types. Of these, the '190' and '191' are single-clock ICs with identical pin-outs and control functions, and the '192' and '193' are dual-clock types with identical pin-outs and control functions (these four counters are also available in 74HC-series CMOS versions, as the 74HC190, 74HC191, 74HC192 and 74HC193).

*Figure 5.31* shows the functional diagrams and pin-outs of the 74LS190 and 74LS191 single-clock 'up/down' counters. These two ICs have very similar active characteristics; namely, they trigger on the rising-edge of the clock signal, and count 'up' when pin-5 is low or 'down' when pin-5 is high (assuming that INH is low and $\overline{PRESET}$ is high); the TC OUT terminal is normally low, but goes high for one clock cycle when the IC reaches its terminal count ('0' in the DOWN mode, or, in the UP mode, '9' in the 74LS190 or '15' in the 74LS191). Note that both ICs have a terminal notated $\overline{RC}$; this 'ripple clock' terminal is normally high but goes low on the falling-

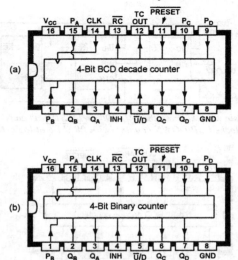

Figure 5.31 *Functional diagrams of the (a) 74LS190 decade and (b) 74LS191 Binary 4-bit UP/DOWN counter ICs.*

edge of the terminal count and goes high again on the next clock rising-edge; the terminal provides a clean clocking signal in multi-stage circuits, and is used as shown in *Figures 5.32* and *5.33*.

*Figure 5.32* shows the basic way of using the '190' or '191' as multi-stage UP/DOWN counters, using ripple-clocking; in essence, the 'ripple clock' signal of the first counter acts as the clock of the second stage, and the 'ripple clock' of that acts as the clock of the third stage, and so on for however many stages there are. *Figure 5.33* shows how to use the counters in the fully synchronous clocking mode; in this case all ICs are clocked in parallel, but the 'ripple clock' output of each stage controls the INH action of the next stage. Note in these two circuits that the 'PRESET' control is not shown,

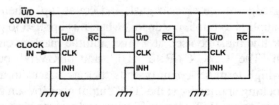

Figure 5.32 *Basic ways of using the 74LS190 or 74LS191 as an N-stage ripple-clocked UP/DOWN counter (with $\overline{PRESET}$ at logic-1).*

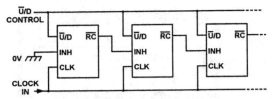

Figure 5.33　*Basic ways of using the 74LS190 or 74LS191 as an N-stage synchronously-clocked UP/DOWN counter (with $\overline{PRESET}$ at logic-1).*

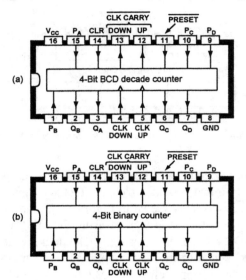

Figure 5.34　*Functional diagrams of the (a) 74LS192 decade and (b) 74LS193 Binary 4-bit dual-clock UP/DOWN counter ICs.*

but should be tied to logic-1 for normal clocked operation.

*Figure 5.34* shows the functional diagrams and pin-outs of the 74LS192 and 74LS193 dual-clock 'up/down' counters. These two ICs also have similar active characteristics; namely, they trigger on the rising-edge of the clock signal, and count 'up' when the clock signal is applied to pin 5, or 'down' when it is applied to pin 4; only one clock line must be used at a time, and the inactive one must be tied high. The CLK CARRY 'UP' and 'DOWN' outputs are normally-high terminal-count outputs that are useful in multi-stage ripple-clocking applications; the 'UP' output goes low on the falling-edge following the 'UP' terminal-count, and returns high on the next rising-edge; the 'DOWN' output similarly goes low, etc., on the

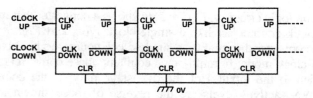

Figure 5.35 *Basic ways of using the 74LS192 or 74LS193 as an N-stage ripple-clocked UP/DOWN counter (with PRESET at logic-1).*

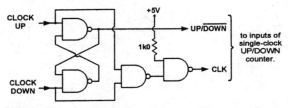

Figure 5.36 *Converter gives dual-clock action on a single-clock UP/DOWN counter.*

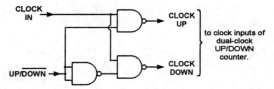

Figure 5.37 *Converter gives single-clock action on a dual-clock UP/DOWN counter.*

'DOWN'terminal-count of '0'. The CLR terminal is normally low, and sets all 'Q'outputs to '0' when taken high; $\overline{\text{PRESET}}$ is normally high, and loads the 'PRESET' data when taken low.

*Figure 5.35* shows the basic way of using the '192' or '193' as multi-stage UP/DOWN counters, using ripple-clocking; here, the 'CLK CARRY' 'UP' and 'DOWN' outputs of the first counter acts as the 'UP' and 'DOWN' clocks of the second stage, and the 'CLK CARRY' outputs of that stage act as the clocks of the third stage, and so on for however many stages there are. Note that the CLR terminal is tied low for normal operation; the PRESET control is not shown, but should be tied to logic-1 for normal clocked operation.

Note that a dual-clock UP/DOWN counter has no special advantage over a single-clock type, nor *vice versa*, and one type can easily be made to act like the other by using suitable input conversion logic circuitry. *Figure 5.36* shows a converter that makes a dual-clock counter act like a single-clock type, and *Figure 5.37* shows a converter that enables a single-clock counter to be driven in the dual-clock mode; in multi-stage counters, these converters must be applied to the input(s) of the first stage only. If the counter's UP/DOWN 'active' levels are the reverse of those shown in the diagrams, simply reverse the input connections to the circuit in *Figure 5.36*, or reverse the output connections from the circuit in *Figure 5.37*.

# 6 Latches, registers, comparators and converters

Data Latches and Shift Registers are widely used members of the flip-flop family of devices, and are often used in conjunction with Logic Comparators and Code Converters. This chapter looks at LS TTL versions of all of these devices and shows how to use them.

## Data latches

Flip-flop circuit elements of the SET-RESET, D-type, and JK types (see Chapter 4) are often called 'latches', because their outputs can be latched into either a logic-0 or logic-1 state by applying suitable input signals. JK and D-type latches are fairly versatile elements, and can be made to act as either data latches or as divide-by-2 circuits by suitably connecting their input and output terminals. A pure 'Data Latch', on the other hand, is an element that is built as a dedicated data latch and can be used for no other purpose; an element of this type acts as a simple memory that can store one 'bit' of binary data for an indefinite period; four such elements can store a complete 4-bit binary 'word'.

A Data Latch stores and outputs whatever logic-level is applied to its 'D' (data) terminal when activated by a suitable 'store' command; the 'store' terminal may be either level or edge sensitive, and *Figure 6.1* shows the basic Data Latch symbols that apply in each case. Level-triggered elements of the type shown in *Figure 6.1a* are 'transparent' when the En (enable) terminal is high (i.e., the Q output follows the D input under this condition), but latch the prevailing D

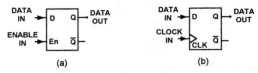

Figure 6.1   *Symbols of (a) level-triggered and (b) edge-triggered Data Latches.*

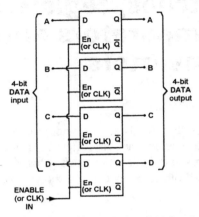

Figure 6.2   *A 4-bit Data Latch is made from four 1-bit Latches connected as shown.*

state into the Q output when En goes low; data can thus be latched by applying a brief positive pulse to the En terminal. Edge-triggered elements of the type shown in *Figure 6.1b* are not transparent, and the Q output ignores the D input until a clock-pulse trigger-edge is applied to the CLK input, at which point the latch stores and outputs the data and holds it until a new clock-pulse arrives.

A 4-bit Data Latch can be built by connecting four 1-bit latches together as shown in *Figure 6.2*, with all En (or CLK) terminals wired in parallel so that all elements activate at the same time. Edge-triggered 4-bit Data Latches are not as useful, popular, or as readily-available as level-triggered types, but can easily be built from JK or D-type flip-flop ICs such as the 74LS73 or 74LS74. Level-triggered 4-bit (or greater) 'transparent' Data Latch ICs are readily available, at very low cost.

Level-triggered 4-bit Data Latches are widely used as temporary memories in digital display-driving applications, and may be used in either of the two basic ways shown in *Figure 6.3*. Assume here that the decade counter shown is one of a cascaded chain of such

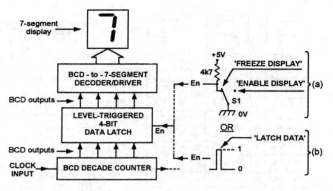

Figure 6.3 *Basic ways of using a level-triggered 4-bit Data Latch in a display-driver application.*

counters, each of which has its BCD outputs fed to a 7-segment digital display via a 4-bit Data Latch and a decoder/driver IC, as shown. In simple counting applications the Data Latch may be used as in *Figure 6.3a*, with its En terminal connected to the +5V rail via a 4k7 resistor so that it is biased high when S1 is set to the ENABLE position but is grounded when S1 is in the FREEZE position. Thus, in the ENABLE position the Latch is transparent, and the counter's state is instantly shown on the display (which may appear as a blur if fast counting is taking place), but when S1 is moved to the FREEZE position the data is immediately latched and the display is effectively frozen (i.e., changes in the counter's states are no longer displayed).

In the alternative control mode shown in *Figure 6.3b*, the Data Latch's En terminal is fed with a timed chain of positive LATCH DATA pulses, and the display thus shows a grabbed snapshot of the counter's instantaneous state each time one of these pulses terminates, and displays it until the arrival of the next pulse's termination point. This technique is useful in cases where the display normally appears as a fast-changing blur; by feeding-in the LATCH DATA pulses at (say) a ten-per-second (100ms) rate, the display can be strobed so that it appears in a varying but clearly readable form. This technique is widely used in digital frequency meters, which use the basic operating principle shown in *Figure 6.4*.

The circuit in *Figure 6.4* is that of a simple 3-digit frequency meter in which the test frequency is fed to the input of the counter chain via a 2-input AND gate, which is controlled via a timebase

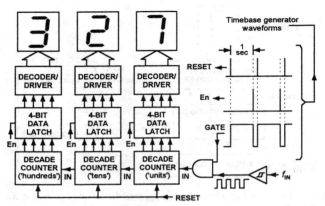

Figure 6.4   *Basic 3-digit digital frequency meter circuit.*

generator that produces a repeating timing cycle. At the start of this cycle the gate is closed, and a brief RESET pulse is fed to all three counters, which clear to zero; the gate then opens, and the counters start to sum the input signal pulses. This count continues for precisely one second, during which the 4-bit Data Latches prevent the counter outputs from reaching the display. At the end of the one-second timing period the GATE closes and terminates the count, and simultaneously an En pulse is fed to the set of Data Latches; this pulse has a width of (say) 100ns or greater, so all the counters have settled down and any glitches have disappeared by the time the En pulse terminates and latches the summed one-second end-count, which is fed to the display and reveals the input test signal's frequency, in Hz (cycles per second). The timing sequence is then complete, but a few moments later it starts to repeat, with the counters resetting and then counting the input pulses for another second, during which time the display gives a steady reading of the results of the previous count, and so on.

The circuit in *Figure 6.4* thus generates a stable 'frequency' display that is regularly updated. In practice, the actual count period can be made any decade multiple or submultiple of one second, provided that the output display is suitably scaled. Thus, on a 3-digit display, a 'count' period of one second gives a maximum frequency reading of 999Hz, and a 1ms period gives a maximum frequency reading of 999kHz, and so on.

## Data Latch ICs

The most popular and readily-available TTL 4-bit 'transparent' or level-triggered Data Latch IC is the 74LS75, which has the functional diagram, etc., shown in *Figure 6.5*. Note the unusual positions of this IC's power supply pins, and also note that the less readily-available 74LS375 4-bit Data Latch IC is internally identical to the 74LS75, but has normal power supply pin allocations, as shown in *Figure 6.6*. Both of these ICs in fact house two independent 2-bit Data Latches, but can be made to function as standard 4-bit

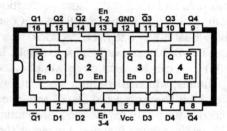

Figure 6.5 *Functional diagram of the 74LS75 4-bit level-triggered Data Latch IC.*

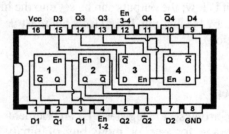

Figure 6.6 *Functional diagram of the 74LS375 4-bit level-triggered Data Latch IC.*

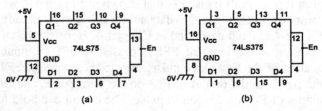

Figure 6.7 *Way of using the (a) 74LS75 or (b) 74LS375 as a basic 4-bit Data Latch.*

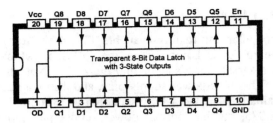

Figure 6.8  *Functional diagram of the 74LS373 8-bit Data Latch IC.*

Data Latches of the *Figure 6.2* type (which are transparent when En is high but latch when En is low) by simply joining their En pins together; *Figures 6.7a* and *b* show the basic connections.

Note that both of these ICs have a full set of Q and $\overline{Q}$ outputs, enabling any individual 4-bit code to be decoded via a 4-input AND (or NAND) gate. The BCD number '9', for example, has the DCBA binary code '1001', so can be decoded by simply ANDing the $Q_D$, $\overline{Q}_C$, $\overline{Q}_B$, and $Q_A$ outputs, which all go high when BCD '9' is present.

If you need an 8-bit level-triggered Data Latch and don't need $\overline{Q}$ outputs, or do need 3-state outputs, the most economical option is to use the 74LS373, which has the functional diagram shown in *Figure 6.8*. This 8-bit latch is transparent when the En terminal is high and latches when it is low; the outputs can be set into the high-impedance (3-state) mode by biasing pin-1 high (this pin must be biased low for normal operation).

## Shift registers

In digital electronics, a 'register' is an element that provides temporary storage for one or more bits of binary data; a 'shift register' is one in which the stored bits can be displaced within the register – one step at a time – by applying suitable clock pulses. The simplest type of shift register is that shown in *Figure 6.9*, which is a synchronous 'bucket brigade' data shifter of the type already shown (in *Figure 4.35*) and described in Chapter 4. Here, the bit of binary data present at the input of FF1 is passed to FF1's output on the application of the first clock pulse, then to the output of FF2 on the second pulse, to the output of FF3 on the third pulse, and finally to the output of FF4 on the fourth pulse. The circuit can hold four bits of data at any given moment, and can store it indefinitely; when the

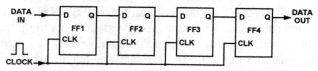

Figure 6.9 *Basic 4-bit serial-in/serial-out (SISO) shift register circuit.*

data is needed, it can be clocked out (in serial form) by applying another set of clock pulses.

Note that the circuit's data in *Figure 6.9* is clocked in and out in serial form, so it is known as a serial-in/serial-out or SISO shift register; it is useful for storing binary signals or delaying them by a fixed number of clock pulses, but not for much else. Its value can be greatly increased by converting it to a serial-in/parallel-out (SIPO)

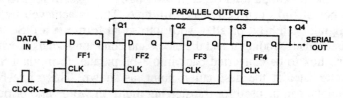

Figure 6.10 *Basic 4-bit serial-in/parallel-out (SIPO) shift register circuit.*

shift register by simply taking the 'parallel' outputs from the Q terminals of all four flip-flops, as shown in *Figure 6.10*; it is then useful for converting serial data into parallel form. This basic type of register can be made to give both serial and parallel outputs by adding a 'serial out' connection as shown dotted in the diagram; such a unit is known as a SIPO/SISO shift register.

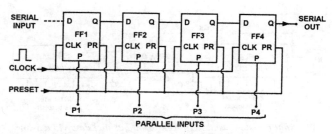

Figure 6.11 *Basic 4-bit parallel-in/serial-out (PISO) shift register circuit.*

The value of the basic shift register can be further increased by fitting it with PRESET terminals, as shown in *Figure 6.11*, so that it can be directly loaded with four bits of parallel data via pins P1 to P4. If the resulting circuit has no serial input facility, it is known as a parallel-in/serial-out (PISO) shift register, but if it does have a serial input facility (as shown dotted in the diagram) it is known as a PISO/SISO shift register. If it is configured to have only parallel-in and parallel-out facilities, it is known as a PIPO shift register. If a register has both parallel and serial inputs and parallel and serial outputs, it is simply called a 'universal' shift register.

*Figure 6.12* shows, in greatly simplified form, one widely-used shift register application. Suppose here that a stack of 8-bit data words needs to be shifted from one point to another; normally, eight data links and one clock and one common link would be needed for this task, making a total of ten links, but by using shift registers the number of links can be reduced to three. This is achieved by first changing each 8-bit parallel word into serial form via a PISO shift register, then sending it and the clock and common signals down the 3-line link to be converted back into 8-bit parallel form via a SIPO shift register at the destination point, as shown. This same basic technique can be used for transferring multi-bit words into or out of modern memory or data processing ICs in which only single IN, OUT, CLK and COMMON pins are allocated to these tasks.

The basic registers of *Figures 6.9* to *6.11* give an action in which the stored data shifts one step to the right on each application of a clock pulse, and are thus known as right-shift registers. But, just as an ordinary counter can be configured to count either up or down, a register can easily be configured to shift data to the right or left, or to have its direction selectable via a control terminal. A large variety of shift register configurations are thus possible, and until the mid-1980s the user was faced with a baffling array of different TTL

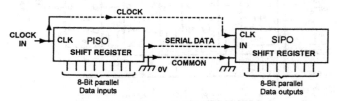

Figure 6.12 *Shift registers used to transfer 8-bit parallel data via a 3-line connection.*

types. Today, however, things are far simpler, since most modern 74LS-series models are of the 'universal' type, one of the few exceptions being the 74LS164 8-bit SIPO shift register. Of the 'universal' types, the 74LS195 is a plain 4-bit type, the 74LS295 and 74LS395 are 4-bit types with 3-state outputs, the 74LS95 and 74LS194 are 4-bit right/left shift types, and the 74LS299 and 74LS323 are 8-bit types with 3-state outputs.

## Logic comparators

A digital 'logic' or 'magnitude' comparator IC is one that compares the binary codes of two words (A and B) of the same bit-size and has outputs that indicate whether code A is greater than, smaller than, or equal to code B. This action is useful in, for example, triggering some action when a counting chain reaches a certain value. The best known TTL IC of this type is the 74LS85 4-bit comparator (see *Figure 6.13*), which can be cascaded with other 74LS85s to make a comparator of any desired bit size. Note that, as well as having four input terminals for each 4-bit word, plus three active-high output terminals (notated A > B, A = B and A < B), this IC also has three input terminals (also notated A > B, A = B and A < B) that are used to implement cascaded operations.

The 74LS85 is very easy to use, as shown in *Figure 6.14*. If only 4-bit words are being compared, a single IC is used, connected in the manner of IC1, with the A > B and A < B cascading terminals grounded and the A = B cascading terminal biased high, and with the three outputs taken from pins 5, 6 and 7. If the words have bit-lengths that are whole-number multiples of four, they can be compared by

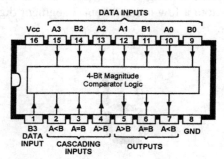

Figure 6.13 *Functional diagram of the 74LS85 4-bit Magnitude comparator IC.*

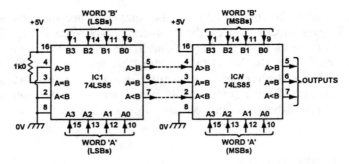

Figure 6.14   *Basic connections for using the 74LS85 'comparator' IC.*

cascading an appropriate number of 74LS85 ICs on a basis of 4-bits per IC (three ICs for 12-bit comparison, etc.); in this case the four least-significant bits (LSBs) must be allocated to IC1, which must be connected in the way already described, and the four most-significant bits (MSBs) must be allocated to the final IC (IC$N$), and so on; in this case, the three outputs of each lower-order IC must be connected to the three 'cascading' inputs of the following IC, the final outputs being taken from the last IC in the chain.

## Code converters

Code converter ICs are widely used in digital electronics to change electronic codes from one format into another. The most widely used device of this type is the BCD to 7-segment decoder/driver IC, which takes the 4-bit BCD-coded output of a counter, etc., and converts it into a form suitable for directly driving a 7-segment LED or LCD digital display. Before looking at specific ICs of this type, however, it is necessary to note a few points about 7-segment digital display basics, as follows.

Figure 6.15   *Standard form and notations of a 7-segment display.*

| SEGMENTS (✓ = ON) | | | | | | | DISPLAY | SEGMENTS (✓ = ON) | | | | | | | DISPLAY |
|---|---|---|---|---|---|---|---|---|---|---|---|---|---|---|---|
| a | b | c | d | e | f | g | | a | b | c | d | e | f | g | |
| ✓ | ✓ | ✓ | ✓ | ✓ | ✓ | | 0 | ✓ | ✓ | ✓ | ✓ | ✓ | ✓ | ✓ | 8 |
| | ✓ | ✓ | | | | | 1 | ✓ | ✓ | ✓ | | | ✓ | ✓ | q |
| ✓ | ✓ | | ✓ | ✓ | | ✓ | 2 | ✓ | ✓ | ✓ | | ✓ | ✓ | ✓ | A |
| ✓ | ✓ | ✓ | ✓ | | | ✓ | 3 | | ✓ | ✓ | ✓ | ✓ | ✓ | ✓ | b |
| | ✓ | ✓ | | | ✓ | ✓ | 4 | ✓ | | | ✓ | ✓ | ✓ | | C |
| ✓ | | ✓ | ✓ | | ✓ | ✓ | 5 | | ✓ | ✓ | ✓ | ✓ | | ✓ | d |
| ✓ | | ✓ | ✓ | ✓ | ✓ | ✓ | 6 | ✓ | | | ✓ | ✓ | ✓ | ✓ | E |
| ✓ | ✓ | ✓ | | | | | 7 | ✓ | | | | ✓ | ✓ | ✓ | F |

Figure 6.16   *Truth Table of a 7-segment display.*

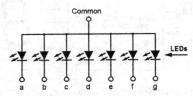

Figure 6.17   *Schematic diagram of a common-anode 7-segment LED display.*

A 7-segment display is a unit that houses seven independently-accessible photoelectric elements such as LEDs or liquid crystals, arranged in the form shown in *Figure 6.15*. The segments are conventionally notated from *a* to *g* in the manner shown, and they can be made to display any number from 0 to 9 or letter from A to F (in a mixture of upper and lower cases) by activating these segments in various combinations, as shown in the Truth Table of *Figure 6.16*.

Practical 7-segment displays need at least eight external connectors, one of which acts as the 'common' terminal. If the display is a LED type, the seven individual LEDs may be arranged as shown in *Figure 6.17*, with all LED anodes connected to the common terminal, or as in *Figure 6.18*, with all LED cathodes connected to the common terminal; in the former case the 7-segment display unit is known as a common-anode type, and in the latter it is called a common-cathode type.

In most practical applications, 7-segment displays are driven – via a suitable decoder/driver IC – from a 4-bit BCD input, and the IC and display are connected as shown in *Figure 6.19*. The IC houses a moderately complex set of logic gates, as is implied by *Figure 6.20*,

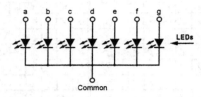

Figure 6.18   *Schematic diagram of a common-cathode 7-segment LED display.*

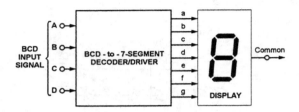

Figure 6.19   *Basic connections of a BCD to 7-segment decoder/driver IC.*

| BCD Signal | | | | DISPLAY | BCD Signal | | | | DISPLAY |
|---|---|---|---|---|---|---|---|---|---|
| D | C | B | A | | D | C | B | A | |
| 0 | 0 | 0 | 0 | *0* | 0 | 1 | 0 | 1 | *5* |
| 0 | 0 | 0 | 1 | *1* | 0 | 1 | 1 | 0 | *6* |
| 0 | 0 | 1 | 0 | *2* | 0 | 1 | 1 | 1 | *7* |
| 0 | 0 | 1 | 1 | *3* | 1 | 0 | 0 | 0 | *8* |
| 0 | 1 | 0 | 0 | *4* | 1 | 0 | 0 | 1 | *9* |

0 = logic low
1 = logic high

Figure 6.20   *Truth Table of a BCD to 7-segment decoder/driver.*

which shows the standard relationship between the BCD input codes
and the displayed 7-segment numerals. In practice, dedicated BCD to
7-segment decoder/driver ICs are usually available in a dedicated
form suitable for driving only a single type of display unit, e.g., a
common-anode LED type, common-cathode LED type, or a liquid-
crystal display (LCD). *Figures 6.21* to *6.23* show the basic ways of
interconnecting each of these IC and display types.

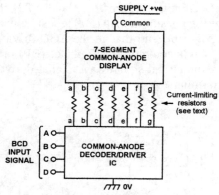

Figure 6.21  *Method of driving a common-anode display.*

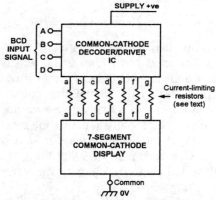

Figure 6.22  *Method of driving a common-cathode display.*

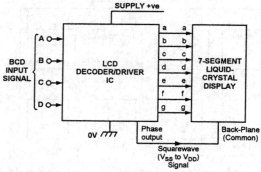

Figure 6.23  *Method of driving a liquid-crystal display.*

Note in the LED circuits (*Figures 6.21* and *6.22*) that in most cases a current-limiting resistor (about 150R) must be wired in series with each display segment, and that in the LCD-driving circuit of *Figure 6.23* the display's common 'back-plane' (BP) terminal must be driven from a symmetrical squarewave signal derived from the IC's phase output terminal.

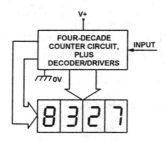

Figure 6.24   *Basic elements of a 4-digit counter/display circuit.*

In reality, 7-segment displays are usually used in multi-digit applications such as that shown in *Figure 6.24*, which shows the basic elements of a 4-digit counter/display circuit that can give a maximum reading of '9999'. Note that if this circuit is used to measure a count of (say) 27 it will actually give a reading of '0027', unless steps are taken to automatically suppress the two (unwanted) leading zeros. Similarly, if the same display is used on a 4-digit voltmeter scaled to read a maximum of 9.999 volts, it will give a reading of 0.100 volts if fed with a 0.1V input, unless steps are taken to suppress the two trailing zeros.

In practice, most modern decoder/driver ICs have facilities for

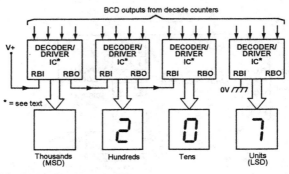

Figure 6.25   *Ripple-blanking used to give leading-zero suppression in a 4-digit counter.*

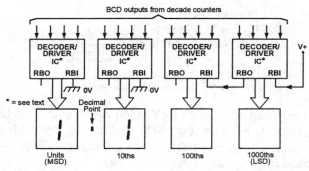

Figure 6.26  *Ripple-blanking used to give trailing-zero suppression in a 4-digit voltmeter.*

giving automatic blanking of leading and/or trailing zeros, using the basic ripple blanking techniques illustrated in *Figures 6.25* and *6.26*. Note in these diagrams that each decoder/driver IC is provided with ripple blanking input (RBI) and output (RBO) terminals; if these terminals are active-high their actions are such that the IC gives normal decoder/driver action and RBO is disabled (driven low) when RBI is biased low, but the display is blanked and RBO is driven high under the 'zero' (BCD input '0000') condition when RBI is biased high. Thus, the RBO terminal is normally low and goes high only if a BCD '0000' input is present at the same time as the RBI terminal is high. With these facts in mind, refer now to *Figures 6.25* and *6.26*.

*Figure 6.25* shows the ripple blanking technique used to provide leading-zero suppression in a 4-digit display that is reading a count of 207. Here, the RBI input of the 'thousands' or MSD decoder/driver IC is tied high, so this display is automatically blanked and RBO is driven high in the presence of a zero. Consequently, RBI of the 'hundreds' IC is driven high under this condition; its display reads '2' and its RBO terminal is thus low. The RBI input of the 'tens' unit is thus also low, so its display reads '0' and its RBO output is low. The least significant digit (LSD) is that of the 'units' readout and does not require zero suppression, so its RBI input is grounded and it reads '7'. The display thus gives an overall reading of '207'.

Note in the *Figure 6.25* leading-zero suppression circuit that ripple blanking feedback is applied backwards, from the MSD to the LSD. *Figure 6.26* shows how trailing zero suppression can be obtained by reversing the direction of feedback, from the LSD to the

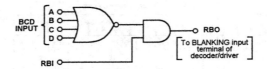

Figure 6.27   *DIY ripple-blanking logic (active-high type).*

MSD. Thus, when an input of 1.1V is fed to this circuit the LSD is blanked, since its BCD input is '0000' and its RBI input is high. Its RBO terminal is high under this condition, so the '100ths' digit is also blanked in the presence of a '0000' input.

Most (but not all) decoder/driver ICs are provided with RBI and RBO ripple blanking terminals; often, these have an active-low action. If a decoder/driver IC does not incorporate a ripple blanking feature, it can usually be obtained by adding external logic similar to that shown in *Figure 6.27*, with the RBO terminal connected to the *blanking* input pin of the decoder/driver IC. In *Figure 6.27* (an active-high circuit), the output of the 4-input NOR gate goes high only in the presence of a '0000' BCD input, and the RBO output goes high only if this input is present while RBI is high.

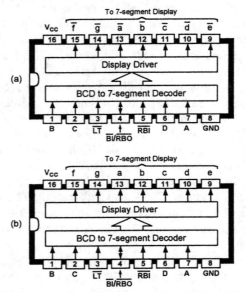

Figure 6.28   *Functional diagrams of the (a) 7447A/74LS47 and (b) 7448/74LS48 BCD to 7-segment decoder/driver ICs.*

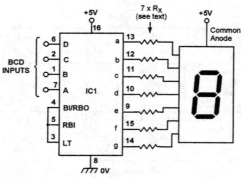

Figure 6.29 *Basic ways of using a 7447A or 74LS47 to drive a common-anode LED display.*

## Decoder/driver ICs

In TTL, the two most popular decoder/driver ICs are the old 7447A and 7448 types and their modern counterparts, the 74LS47 and 74LS48. These ICs are functionally very similar, as can be seen from *Figures 6.28a* and *b*; all four ICs have integral ripple-blanking facilities. The 7447A/74LS47 has an active-low output and is specifically designed for driving a common-anode LED display via external current-limiting resistors $R_x$ (typically 150R), as shown in *Figure 6.29*. The 7448/74LS48 has an active-high output designed for driving a common-cathode LED display in a manner similar to that of *Figure 6.29*, but with the display's common terminal taken to

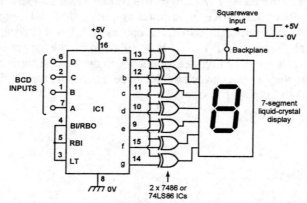

Figure 6.30 *Basic ways of using the 7448 or 74LS48 to drive a liquid-crystal display.*

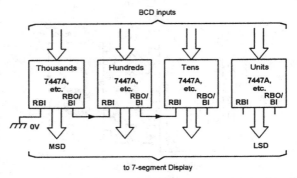

Figure 6.31   *Method of applying leading-zero suppression to the first three digits of a 4-digit display, using 7447A or 74LS47 ICs.*

ground. In all cases, the $R_X$ current-limiting resistors must be chosen to hold the segment currents below the following absolute limits:

$$4774A = 40mA \quad 74LS47 = 24mA \quad 7448/74LS48 = 6mA.$$

*Figure 6.30* shows how the 7448/74LS48 can be used to drive a liquid-crystal display (LCD), using a pair of 7486 or 74LS86 Quad 2-input EX-OR gate ICs and an external 50Hz squarewave to apply the necessary phase drive signals to the display, as already described.

Note from *Figure 6.28* that each of these ICs has three active-low input 'control' terminals, these being designated $\overline{LT}$ (Lamp Test), $\overline{BI/RBO}$, and $\overline{RBI}$. The $\overline{LT}$ terminal drives all display terminals on when it is driven low when the $\overline{BI/RBO}$ terminal is open-circuit or high. When the $\overline{BI/RBO}$ terminal is pulled low all outputs are blanked; this terminal also functions as a ripple-blanking output terminal. *Figure 6.31* shows how to connect the ripple-blanking terminals to give leading-zero suppression on the first three digits of a 4-digit display (this basic circuit can be used with any IC within the 7447/7448 family of devices).

# 7 Special purpose ICs and circuits

So far, this book has dealt with purely run-of-the mill TTL ICs such as logic gates, flip-flops, counters, latches, and other devices of the type that – if you are a professional digital circuit designer – you are likely to use on a regular basis. But there are other useful types of TTL IC that you may need to use only very rarely, and amongst them are Multiplexers, Decoders and Demultiplexers, Addressable Latches, Full-Adders, and Bus Transceivers. This final Chapter explains how to use these types of special-purpose ICs, and concludes by giving functional descriptions of a few other unusual and very rarely-used types of TTL IC.

## Multiplexing basics

A multiplexer is a device that enables two or more signals to be selected and combined into a single output that can subsequently be demultiplexed in a way that enables the original signals to be retrieved. *Figure 7.1* illustrates the basic principle of a multiplexing system. Imagine here that the two switches are motor driven and con-

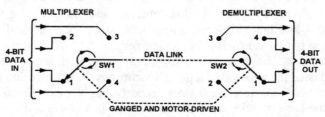

Figure 7.1 *Basic principles of a multiplexed data transfer system.*

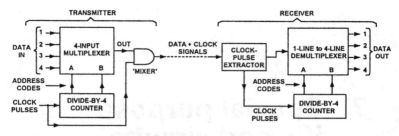

Figure 7.2   *Basic circuit of a multiplexed data transfer system.*

tinuously rotate and are somehow remotely ganged so that SW2 is in position '1' when SW1 is in position '1', and so on; consequently, the 4-bit data from the four input lines is repeatedly sequentially inspected via SW1 and converted into serial form (multiplexed), and then shoved down the data link to SW2, where it is demultiplexed and reappears in its original 4-bit form on four separate output lines. The big feature of this system is, of course, that it enables a whole stack of parallel data to be transmitted – in serial form – via a single data link such as an electric or fibre-optic cable or a wireless carrier wave.

*Figure 7.2* shows, in greatly simplified form, an electronic version of the above circuit. Here, at the transmitter end of the system, SW1 is replaced by a 4-input multiplexer, the action of which is such that any of the four data input lines can be coupled to the OUT line by applying a suitable 2-bit binary address code (00, 01, 10 or 11). These codes are generated sequentially by the divide-by-4 counter (consisting of two cascaded divide-by-2 flip-flops), which is driven by a clock-pulse generator that produces narrow trigger pulses. The outputs of the multiplexer and the clock-pulse generator are mixed together in the 2-input AND gate and transmitted down the single data link; at the receiver end of the system, the clock pulses are extracted from the data link and used to drive another divide-by-4 counter that generates address codes for the 1-line to 4-line demultiplexer, which reconstructs the original input data and puts it out on four separate lines.

The above circuit is, of course, greatly simplified, and in practice would need the addition of a pulse synchronization system and a few other refinements to make it work properly, but it does serve to illustrate the basic multiplexing principle. Note in particular that multiplexers and demultiplexers are really meant to form individual elements in a highly specialized type of system, but that in practice a multiplexer actually functions as an addressable data selector (like SW1 in *Figure 7.1*), and a demultiplexer functions as an addressable data distributor (like SW2 in *Figure 7.1*) or as a binary-code 'decoder', and in these modes both types of device are so useful that they are usually described as 'multiplexer/data-selector' and 'demultiplexer/decoder' ICs.

Note in *Figure 7.1* that SW1 and SW2 can both pass signals in either direction, and can thus be used as either multiplexers or demultiplexers by simply placing them in the appropriate part of the system. TTL ICs, however, can only pass signals in one direction, and make such poor imitations of electro-mechanical switches that they have to be produced in both 'multiplexer' and 'demultiplexer' versions. CMOS ICs, on the other hand, can be made to act as near-perfect bidirectional switches that can handle both digital and analogue signals; CMOS 'analogue switches' can thus be used as both multiplexers and demultiplexers, but for many years were too slow for use in most TTL-type applications. Then, in the mid-1980s, the 74HC series of fast CMOS was introduced, and its superb range of 'analogue switch' ICs quickly made many of the existing TTL multiplexer and demultiplexer ICs obsolescent, the upshot being that relatively few of these devices are now available in TTL form. The next two sections of this chapter describe some of the TTL types that remain, and the third section describes some of the 74HC-series 'analogue switch' ICs that are available.

## TTL multiplexer ICs

The three best known types of current-production TTL multiplexer IC are the 74LS157 Quad 2-input IC, the 74LS153 Dual 4-input IC, and the 74LS151 8-input IC. *Figure 7.3* shows the functional diagram of the 74LS157, which effectively houses four ganged 2-way ('A' or 'B') switches with buffered outputs that can be disabled (driven low) by biasing INH pin 15 high; the switch positions can be selected via pin 1, which selects position 'A' when biased low or 'B' when biased high. The 74LS157 is very easy to use, and *Figure 7.4* shows how to connect it as a data-selector that can select either of two 4-bit input words via pin-1. This circuit is useful in applications where – for example – either of two 4-bit codes need to be sent to the PRESET terminal of a counter/divider IC, etc.

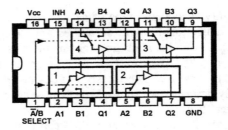

Figure 7.3   *Functional diagram of the 74LS157 Quad 2-input data-selector/multiplexer IC.*

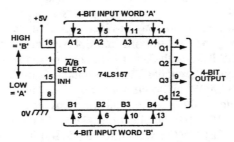

Figure 7.4   *Normal connections for using the 74LS157 as a 4-bit data-word selector.*

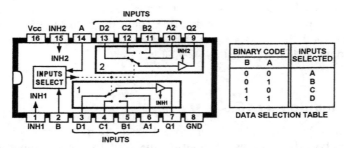

Figure 7.5   *Functional diagram and Data Selection Table of the 74LS153 Dual 4-input Data Selector/Multiplexer IC.*

*Figure 7.5* shows the functional diagram of the 74LS153, which effectively houses two ganged 4-way ('A' to 'D') switches with buffered outputs that can be disabled (driven low) by biasing the appropriate INH terminal (pins 1 or 15) high; the switch positions can be selected by applying the appropriate 'BA' binary codes to pins 2 and 14, as indicated in the table in *Figure 7.5*. *Figure 7.6* shows how to connect the IC as a Dual 4-way input selector, in which each 'switch' outputs the input data that is selected via the BA

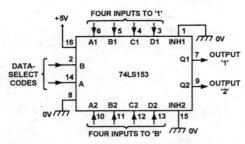

Figure 7.6  *Normal connections for using the 74LS153 as a Dual 4-way input selector.*

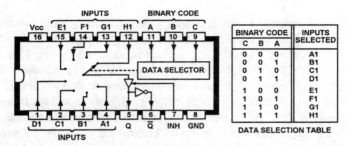

Figure 7.7  *Functional diagram and Data Selection Table of the 74LS151 8-input Data Selector/Multiplexer IC.*

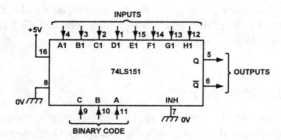

Figure 7.8  *Normal connections for using the 74LS151 as an 8-way input selector.*

'select' code. Note that the IC can be used as a Dual 2-bit decoder by applying the 2-bit code to the BA terminals and tying all but one of each switch's four inputs low, so that the switch's output goes high only when the desired 2-bit code is present, as indicated in the IC's Data Selection Table; thus, the '10' BA code can be detected by tying only the 'C' input high, etc.

*Figure 7.7* shows the functional diagram of the 74LS151, which

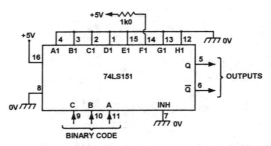

Figure 7.9 *Normal connections for using the 74LS151 as a 3-bit decoder (shown set for '101' decoding).*

effectively houses a single 8-way ('A1' to 'H1') switch with a buffered output that can be disabled (driven low) by biasing the INH terminal high; the switch positions can be selected by applying the appropriate 'CBA' 3-bit binary codes to pins 9-10-11, as indicated in the table in *Figure 7.7*. *Figure 7.8* shows how to connect the IC as an 8-way input selector, which outputs whichever switch input is selected via the CBA 'select' code; a direct output is available on pin-5, and an inverted one on pin 6. Alternatively, *Figure 7.9* shows the IC wired as a 3-bit decoder, with the 3-bit code applied to the CBA terminals and with all but one of the eight inputs tied low, so that the pin 5 output goes high only when the desired 3-bit code is present (see the *Figure 7.7* Data Selection Table); the IC is shown connected to detect the '101' code, which selects the F1 input, which in this case is tied high.

## TTL demultiplexer ICs

The three best known types of current-production TTL decoder/demultiplexer ICs are the 74LS139 Dual 4-output IC, the 74LS138 8-output IC, and the 74LS154 16-output IC, which all have active-low outputs. *Figure 7.10* shows the functional diagram of the 74LS139, which effectively houses two independent 4-way ('A̅' to 'D̅') selectors with active-low buffered outputs that can all be disabled (driven high) by biasing the INH terminal high; the switch positions are selected via a 2-bit BA binary code, as shown in the diagram's Decoding Table. The 74LS139 can be used as a Dual 2-bit 4-way (2-line to 4-line) decoder by connecting it as shown in *Figure 7.11*, with the INH terminals grounded and the decoded outputs

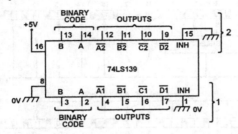

Figure 7.10 *Functional diagram and Decoding Table of the 74LS139 Dual 4-way decoder/demultiplexer IC.*

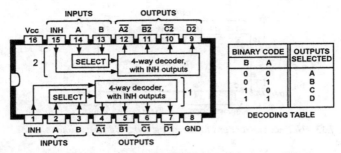

Figure 7.11 *Normal connections for using the 74LS139 as a Dual 2-line to 4-line decoder.*

taken from the appropriate output terminals (see the IC's Decoding Table); thus, the C output is normally high, and goes low only in the presence of a '10' BA input code, etc. The IC can be used as a demultiplexer by using the INH terminal as the data input.

*Figure 7.12* shows the functional diagram and Decoding Table of the 74LS138, which effectively houses an 8-way selector with

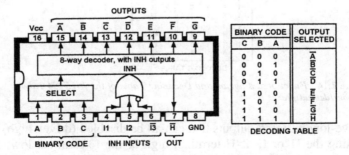

Figure 7.12 *Functional diagram and Decoding Table of the 74LS138 8-way decoder/demultiplexer IC.*

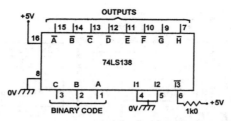

Figure 7.13   *Normal connections for using the 74LS138 as a 3-line to 8-line decoder.*

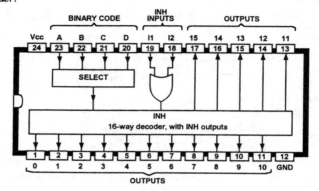

Figure 7.14   *Functional diagram and Decoding Table of the 74LS154 16-way decoder/demultiplexer IC.*

active-low buffered outputs that can all be disabled (driven high) by biasing the I1 or I2 INH terminal high or the $\overline{I3}$ terminal low; the switch positions are selected via a 3-bit CBA binary code, as shown in the diagram's Decoding Table. The 74LS138 can be used as a 3-

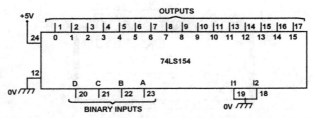

Figure 7.15 *Normal connections for using the 74LS154 as a 4-line to 16-line decoder.*

bit 8-way (3-line to 8-line) decoder by connecting it as shown in *Figure 7.13*, with the decoded outputs taken from the appropriate output terminals (see the IC's Decoding Table); each output is normally high, but goes low when activated by its 3-bit 'select' code. This IC can be used as a demultiplexer by using one of the active-low INH terminals as the data input, with the other two INH inputs disabled.

Finally, *Figure 7.14* shows the functional diagram and Decoding Table of the 24-pin 74LS154, which effectively houses a 16-way selector with active-low buffered outputs that can all be disabled (driven high) by biasing either of the two INH terminals high; the switch positions are selected via a 4-bit DCBA binary code, as shown in the Decoding Table. The 74LS154 can be used as a 4-bit 16-way (4-line to 16-line) decoder by connecting it as in *Figure 7.15*, with the decoded outputs taken from the appropriate output terminals (see the IC's Decoding Table); each output is normally high, but goes low when activated by its 4-bit 'select' code. *Figure 2.9* (in Chapter 2) shows an example of this IC used in a circuit that generates a logic-1 output when any of four pre-designated 4-bit input codes are present. The 74LS154 can be used as a demultiplexer by tying one INH input low and using the other INH terminal as a Data input.

## CMOS 'analogue switch' IC

TTL elements can pass signal currents efficiently in only one direction and thus make rather poor imitations of electro-mechanical switches, which are inherently bidirectional devices. Some CMOS elements, on the other hand, can be made to act as near-perfect bi-directional switches, and for many years a range of excellent 4000-

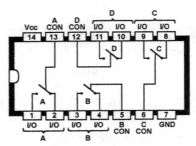

Figure 7.16   *Functional diagram of the 74HC4066 Quad bilateral switch IC.*

series CMOS 'analogue switch' ICs have been available. Many of these ICs have also been produced in fast 74HC-series versions since the mid-1980s, and can easily be used to replace existing TTL multiplexer and demultiplexer ICs in many applications.

The simplest of these 74HC-series 'analogue switch' ICs is the 74HC4066, which acts like four independent bidirectional ON/OFF switches, each of which has a near-infinite OFF resistance and a 50R ON resistance that can comfortably pass currents of up to 20mA when the IC is operated from a 5V supply. *Figure 7.16* shows the IC's functional diagram; note in particular that – in common with the rest of the CMOS 'analogue switch' family – either end of each CMOS switch can be used as an IN or OUT terminal, and is thus usually notated 'in/out' or 'I/O' on function diagrams. The IC's basic action is such that each switch is open (OFF) when its CON (control) terminal is low, and is closed (ON) when the CON terminal is high.

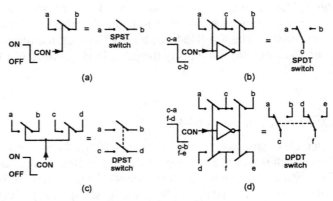

Figure 7.17   *Four basic ways of using 74HC4066 switching elements.*

*Figure 7.17* shows four basic ways of using the 74HC4066's switching elements. In *Figure 7.17a*, an element is used as a basic SPST (single-pole single-throw) ON/OFF switch, and operates in the way described above. In *Figure 7.17b*, two switches have their CON terminals driven in anti-phase, and function as a SPDT switch; *Figure 7.17c* shows a ganged dual version of the circuit in *Figure 7.17a*, and *Figure 7.17d* is a ganged dual version of *Figure 7.17b* but with both 'SPDT' switches sharing a common CON-drive inverting element.

The most widely used variants of 74HC-series CMOS 'analogue switch' ICs are those that are described in the manufacturer's data sheets as 'multiplexer/demultiplexer ICs', but which are better described as multi-way bilateral electronic switches. Chief amongst these are the 74HC4051 8-channel IC, the 74HC4052 Dual 4-channel IC, the 74HC4053 Triple 2-channel IC, and the 74HC4067 16-channel IC, which can be regarded as 8-way, Dual 4-way, Triple 2-way, and 16-way switches respectively. *Figure 7.18* shows the functional diagram of the 74HC4051, which has basic characteristics

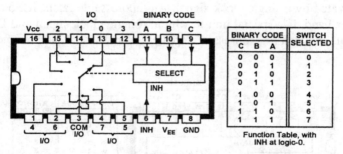

| BINARY CODE | | | SWITCH SELECTED |
|---|---|---|---|
| C | B | A | |
| 0 | 0 | 0 | 0 |
| 0 | 0 | 1 | 1 |
| 0 | 1 | 0 | 2 |
| 0 | 1 | 1 | 3 |
| 1 | 0 | 0 | 4 |
| 1 | 0 | 1 | 5 |
| 1 | 1 | 0 | 6 |
| 1 | 1 | 1 | 7 |

Function Table, with INH at logic-0.

Figure 7.18 *Functional diagram and Table of the 74HC4051 8-channel multiplexer/demultiplexer IC.*

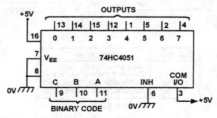

Figure 7.19 *Normal connections for using the 74HC4051 as a 3-line to 8-line decoder with active-high outputs.*

that are shared by the whole family, i.e., switch positions are selected via a binary code (3-bit in this case), all switches can be disabled (made to act like open circuits) by driving the INH terminal high, and the IC has a $V_{EE}$ supply terminal that must be shorted to GND in digital application. *Figure 7.19* shows the 74HC4051 wired as a 3-line to 8-line decoder; it is given active-high outputs by shorting the COM I/O terminal to the +5V rail; it can be given active-low outputs by shorting the COM I/O terminal to ground.

Note that the 74HC4051, 74HC4052, 74HC4053, and 74HC4067 are functionally identical to standard 4051, 4052, 4053, and 4067 CMOS ICs, and all of these devices are comprehensively described in the author's *CMOS Circuits Manual* in the Newnes 'Circuits Manual' series.

## Addressable latches

Chapter 6 gives a reasonably full description of conventional Data latch ICs, in which groups of latch elements are ganged together and activated by a single clock signal. An 'addressable latch' IC, on the other hand, is a special unit in which a single clock signal and Data input, etc., can be 'addressed' (applied) to individual latch elements

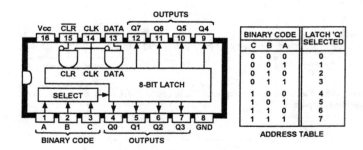

Figure 7.20 *Functional diagram, Address Table, and Function Table of the 74LS259 8-bit addressable latch IC.*

amongst a group, one at a time; the 'address' takes the form of a binary code (2-bits for four latches, 3-bits for eight latches). The best known LS TTL IC of this type is the 74LS259 8-bit addressable latch; *Figure 7.20* shows its functional diagram, Address Table, and Function Table. This IC has four basic operating modes (see the Function Table), as follows:

(1) When $\overline{\text{CLR}}$ is low and CLK is high, all latches are cleared and the Q0 to Q7 outputs go low.
(2) When $\overline{\text{CLR}}$ and CLK are low, the IC acts as a 3-line to 8-line decoder (or demultiplexer) in which the selected output is active-high and all other outputs are low.
(3) When $\overline{\text{CLR}}$ is high and CLK is low, the IC acts as an addressable transparent latch, in which the Q-output of the selected latch follows the Data input, and all other latches remain in their previous states.
(4) When $\overline{\text{CLR}}$ and CLK are high, the current Data is latched into the selected latch.

The 74LS259 is thus a reasonably versatile unit that can be used as an 8-bit serial-in to parallel-out converter, as a general-purpose

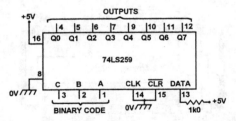

Figure 7.21  *Connections for using the 74LS259 as a 3-line to 8-line decoder with active-high outputs.*

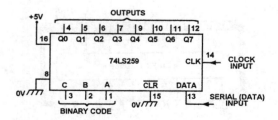

Figure 7.22  *Connections for using the 74LS259 as an 8-bit demultiplexer.*

memory unit, or as a decoder or demultiplexer, etc. *Figure 7.21* shows it used as a 3-line to 8-line decoder that drives the selected output high in the presence of the correct address code, and *Figure 7.22* shows it used as an 8-bit demultiplexer, with the serial input applied to the Data terminal and the clock signal (which would also drive the 3-stage counter that generates the CBA binary 'select' code) applied to the CLK terminal.

# Full-adder ICs

The basic principles of binary half-adder and full-adder circuits are outlined in Chapter 2 (see *Figures 2.76* to *2.78*). The two best known TTL ICs of the latter type are the 74LS83 and 74LS283 4-bit full-adders, which are functionally identical but have different pin-outs, as shown in *Figures 7.23* and *7.24*. Each of these ICs generates a 4-bit plus CARRY output equal to the sum ('S') of two 4-bit (DCBA) input words ('1' and '2'); numbers of these ICs can be coupled together to carry out binary addition on words of any desired bit size, typically taking 25ns to add two 8-bit words, or 45ns to add two 16-bit words.

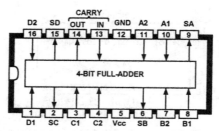

Figure 7.23   *Functional diagram of the 74LS83 4-bit full-adder IC.*

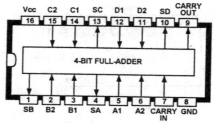

Figure 7.24   *Functional diagram of the 74LS283 4-bit full-adder IC.*

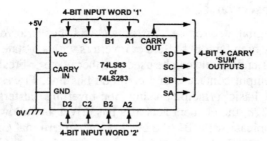

Figure 7.25 *Normal circuit for using the 74LS83 or 74LS283 as a 4-bit full-adder.*

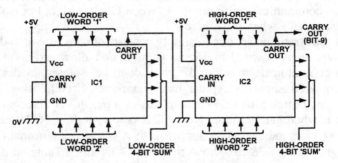

Figure 7.26 *Way of using the 74LS83 or 74LS283 as an 8-bit full-adder.*

*Figure 7.25* shows the basic way of using the 74LS83 or 74LS383 as a single 4-bit adder; the CARRY IN terminal is tied low, word '1' is applied to one set of input terminals and word '2' is applied to the other, and the result of the addition appears on the 'S' output terminals. If the result of the addition is greater than decimal 15 (binary 1111), the CARRY OUT terminal goes to logic-1, and thus acts as a bit-5 output.

*Figure 7.26* shows how to interconnect two 4-bit full-adders to make an 8-bit adder. The least-significant four bits of each input word are applied to IC1, which has its CARRY IN terminal tied low, and the four most-significant bits are applied to IC2, which has its CARRY IN terminal tied to the CARRY OUT of IC1. IC1 provides the four least-significant bits of the resulting sum, and IC2 provides the four most-significant bits plus a CARRY OUT, which acts as bit-9. This basic circuit can be expanded upwards to accept input words of any desired bit size by taking the CARRY OUT of each successive lower-order stage to the CARRY IN terminal of the next higher-order stage in the chain.

## Bus transceiver ICs

In TTL digital electronics, 'bus driver' and 'bus receiver' elements are simply high fan-out buffers or inverters with a 3-state output (see Chapters 1 and 2), and can be used to either make or break a circuit's input or output contact with a common bus line. *Figure 7.27* illustrates the basic principle, using non-inverting buffers. Thus, in *Figure 7.27a*, the element acts as a bus driver and allows point 'A' to communicate with 'B' (the bus line) when terminal GAB is high, but is put into the high-impedance 3-state mode when GAB is low. In *Figure 7.27b*, the element acts as a bus receiver and allows the bus (B) to communicate with point 'A' when GBA is high, but isolates the two points when GBA is low.

A 'bus transceiver' circuit simply consists of a bus driver and bus receiver element wired in inverse parallel, and allows points A and B to communicate in either direction or to be isolated, as desired. *Figure 7.28* shows a typical bus transceiver circuit, using non-inverting buffers; the L/H element acts as a bus driver and connects A to B when gate terminal NOT-GBA is low, and the R/H element acts as a bus receiver and connects B to A when gate terminal GBA is high. *Figure 7.28* also shows the circuit's Function Table; thus, the transceiver connects B to A when both gates are high, and connects A to B when both gates are low, and isolates both points when NOT-

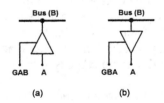

Figure 7.27   *3-state buffers used as (a) bus driver and (b) bus receiver elements.*

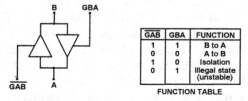

| GAB | GBA | FUNCTION |
|-----|-----|----------|
| 1 | 1 | B to A |
| 0 | 0 | A to B |
| 1 | 0 | Isolation |
| 0 | 1 | Illegal state (unstable) |

FUNCTION TABLE

Figure 7.28   *Typical non-inverting bus transceiver circuit and Function Table.*

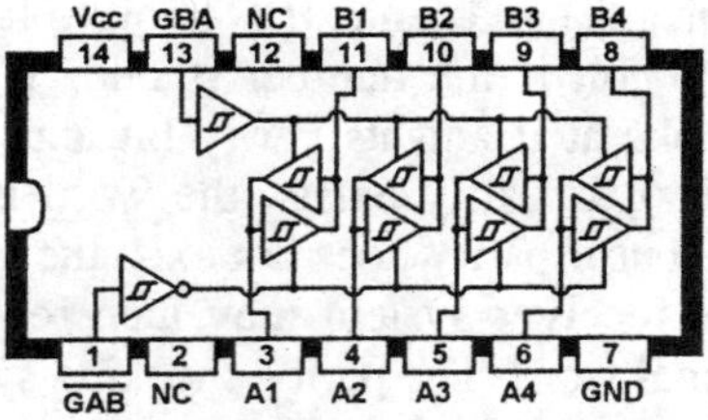

Figure 7.29 *Functional diagram of the 74LS243 non-inverting 4-line bus transceiver IC.*

GAB is high and GBA is low. Note that the GBA-high/NOT-GAB-low condition is an illegal one; it turns both elements on, effectively shorting their outputs and inputs together, and possibly causing latch-up or wild oscillations.

The three best-known LS TTL bus transceiver ICs are the 74LS242, 74LS243 and 74LS245. The 74LS242 (inverting) and 74LS243 (non-inverting) ICs are 4-line transceivers with identical outlines and pin notations; *Figure 7.29* shows the functional diagram of the 74LS243, which has a Function Table identical to that shown in *Figure 7.28*. The 74LS245 is an 8-line non-inverting transceiver that incorporates logic circuitry that makes it impossible for an 'illegal' input gating state to occur; this IC is housed in a 20-pin DIL package.

## Miscellaneous TTL IC types

All of the most important basic types of current-production TTL ICs have now been covered in this book, but there are still a few types of TTL IC that have not yet been mentioned, because they are obsolescent or obsolete and may only be found in older equipment, or are unduly expensive or hard to find, or may best be available in CMOS or some other technology, etc. Included amongst these are the following devices:

*Parity generators/checkers.* Whenever a digital word is transmitted along a severely interference-prone communication link it is possible that the word may be so degraded that its code is changed from that transmitted. Parity generator/checker ICs offer a simple means of checking the truth of a word's code, via an extra 'parity' bit; when the word is to be transmitted, the IC looks at the number of '1's that it contains and (typically) adds an extra '1' bit to it if the number is even, or an extra '0' bit if the number is odd. When the word is received, the IC looks at it and its parity bit and checks them for compatability (parity); if parity exists, the word is assumed to be pure, and is passed, but if parity does not exist the word is proven to be corrupt, and the receiver system may then request the retransmission of the original word. The parity-checking system is not foolproof, but does offer a very high level of security. The best-known current-production TTL IC of this type is the 74180 9-bit (8 data bits plus 1 parity bit) Parity Generator/Checker, which uses Standard TTL technology.

*Priority encoders.* These are multi-input (usually 8 or 10 line) 3-bit encoders in which the inputs are ranked in order of priority so that – at any given moment – the IC outputs the 3-bit code of only the highest ranked applied input. Thus, if inputs 1, 5 and 7 are applied simultaneously, the IC will output the '7' code until input-7 is removed, and will then output the '5' code until input-5 is removed, and so on. ICs of this type help a system to deal with problems/tasks in a sensible order of importance. The best-known current production TTL ICs of this type are the 74LS147 decimal-to-BCD and 74LS148 Binary 8-line to 3-line Priority Encoders.

*RAMs and ROMs.* In the early days of TTL, the '74'-series list of digital ICs fairly bristled with a range of 'memory' devices such as RAMs (Random Access Memories), ROMs (Read Only Memories), FIFOs (First-In First-Out memories), etc. In fact, twenty-five of the first three hundred TTL IC types issued were devices of these kinds. In subsequent years, however, far more efficient technologies were evolved and used in the making of memory elements, and as a consequence TTL memory ICs now rarely appear in current-production lists of '74'-series ICs.

*Rate multipliers.* These are a special type of programmable divider, in which the divide-by value equals $B/X$, where $X$ is a settable limited-range whole-number value and $B$ is a fixed base number (either 10 or 64); thus, if $B = 10$ and $X$ is set at 7, the IC will output seven pulses for every ten that are applied at the input and have a divide-by value of 1.4286; if $X$ is stepped through numbers 1 to 9, the IC output will provide 1 to 9 pulses for every 10 input pulses, and have divide-by values that step through the values 10, 5, 3.333, 2.5,

2, 1.667, 1.4286, 1.25 and 1.111. ICs of this type are (or used to be) useful in performing arithmetic operations such as multiplication and division, and in A-to-D and D-to-A conversion, etc., but have now been generally superseded by more sophisticated types of LSI device. The best-known TTL Rate Multiplier ICs are the 7497 6-bit Binary Rate Multiplier, which has a base number of 64 and can accept any $X$ number from 1 to 63 (set via a 6-bit Address), and the 74167 Decade Rate Multiplier, which has a base number of 10 and can accept any $X$ number from 1 to 9 (set via a 4-bit Address).

*Voltage controlled oscillators (VCOs).* The best-known TTL IC of this type is the 74LS629 Dual VCO, which can be used at frequencies ranging from 1Hz to 20MHz. This IC is rather expensive, however, and should only be used as a last resort, when no cheaper alternative (such as the VCO section of the CMOS 4046 or 74HC4046 PLL IC) is available.

# Index